Library of Congress Cataloging-in-Publication Data

Schultz, James, 1956–
    Crafting flight : Aircraft pioneers and the contributions of the men and
women of NASA Langley Research Center / by James Schultz.
        p. cm. -- (NASA history series)
    "SP-2003-4316."
    Includes bibliographical references and index.
    1. Langley Research Center. 2. Aeronautical engineering--United States--History. 3.
Aeronautical engineers--United States. I. Title. II. Series.

TL862.L35 S38 2003
629.13'00973--dc21

                                                              2002026358

For sale by U.S. Government Printing Office
Superintendent of Documents, Mail Stop: SSOP, Washington, DC 20402-9328
ISBN 0-16-051410-X

Front cover shows the Wright Brothers' historic flight
and an artist's concept of a future aircraft.

Pearl Young at work in Instrument
Research Division, c. 1929
(on facing page).

NASA Langley photo no. EL-2000-00347

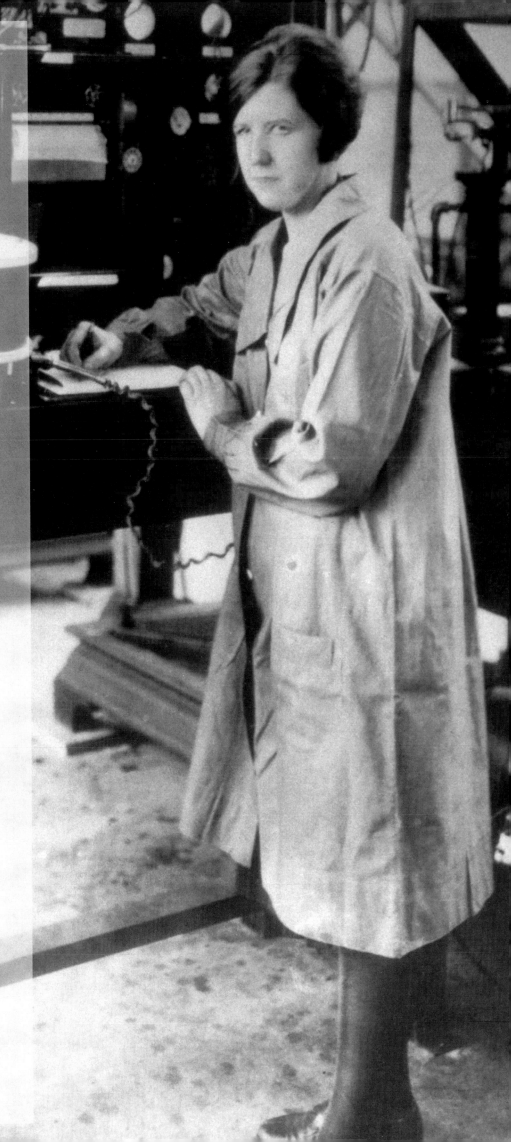

CRAFTING FLIGHT

BY
JAMES SCHULTZ

AIRCRAFT PIONEERS AND
THE CONTRIBUTIONS OF
THE MEN AND WOMEN OF
NASA LANGLEY RESEARCH CENTER

SP-2003-4316

7- by 10-Foot Atmospheric Wind Tunnel in 1931.

CONTENTS

LANGLEY RESEARCH CENTER

Lunar Landing Research Vehicle outside Langley hanger,
later shipped to Houston to train Apollo astronauts.

GRIN photo no. GPN-2000-001821

PREFACE

While this is a self-contained history of NASA Langley Research Center's contributions to flight, many other organizations around the country played a vital role in the work described in this book.

Within the Agency, Langley for decades has worked closely with other NASA Centers, particularly Ames Research Center at Moffett Field, California; Glenn Research Center in Cleveland, Ohio; and Dryden Flight Research Center in Edwards, California. These are NASA's "aero" centers, where most of the Agency's aeronautics research has been conducted over the years.

Other NASA Centers include Marshall Space Flight Center in Huntsville, Alabama; Goddard Space Flight Center in Greenbelt, Maryland; Kennedy Space Center in Cape Canaveral, Florida; Johnson Space Center in Houston, Texas; and Stennis Space Center in Mississippi.

Without the support of these Centers and NASA Headquarters in Washington, D.C., Langley's work would not have been possible. NASA also collaborates extensively with academia, private industry, and other government agencies. These are far too numerous to mention, but their contributions are equally important.

Last but certainly not least, we must not forget the U.S. citizen, whose tax dollars support our work and whose representation in the Administration and the Congress guides our actions. It is for their benefit, ultimately, that we exist.

**Researcher in the Langley Immersive Design
and Simulator Laboratory.**

FOREWORD

One hundred years of flight is quite a historical achievement. We have progressed from a 57-second flight over the dunes of Kitty Hawk to the over 25-year journeys of *Voyager 1* and *2* beyond Pluto's orbit. During that time span, in perhaps the most awe-inspiring aerospace accomplishment after Wilbur and Orville Wright's historic flight, the first humans, Neil Armstrong, Buzz Aldrin, and Michael Collins, flew to the Moon. Sixty-six years after the flight at Kitty Hawk, people all across our home planet Earth paused to watch on television as American astronaut Neil Armstrong stepped out of the Lunar Lander onto the surface of the Moon.

As we pause to celebrate the centennial of flight from our perspective in the early part of the twenty-first century, we can look back over the countless contributions of many individuals to flight. The first person who looked to the sky, observed birds in flight, and dreamed of humans soaring through the air is lost in history. Recounted in these pages are the stories of a few aviation pioneers and the contributions of the men and women of Langley Research Center. We celebrate not only their accomplishments, but also their perseverance and dedication.

A Congressional mandate issued in 1915 formed the National Advisory Committee for Aeronautics (NACA). In 1958, Congress mandated the National Aeronautics and Space Administration (NASA) from the NACA. Both the NACA and NASA were created in response to the need for the United States to catch up to existing technological advances. Although the United States was the birthplace of controlled, powered flight, by World War I, we were technologically far behind Germany, France, and Great Britain. The NACA was created to study the problems of flight "with a view to their practical solution." In 1958 when the former Soviet Union launched the first artificial satellite to orbit the Earth, the United States again found itself behind technologically, Congress passed the National Aeronautics and Space Administration Act of 1958 "to provide for research into problems of flight within and outside the Earth's atmosphere."

Today through partnerships with industry, universities and colleges, and other government agencies, NASA continues to conduct scientific research and exploration and to develop cutting-edge technologies to advance national leadership in aeronautics and space activities. Through painstaking diligent research, careful examination of data, and thoughtful formulation of theories, NASA employees are pushing the extent of our knowledge of aeronautics and astronautics, and many other branches of science as well.

Building on an extraordinary record of accomplishment, the people of NASA continue to develop revolutionary technologies that contribute significantly to the safety, reliability, efficiency, and speed of air transportation and advance the knowledge and understanding of our home planet, Earth.

Delma C. Freeman, Jr.
Director
NASA Langley Research Center

Jeremiah F. Creedon and Richard Culpepper unveil plaque honoring Langley as a historic aerospace site.

INTRODUCTION

When you pass through the front gates of NASA Langley Research Center you are entering an extraordinary place. You could easily miss that fact, however. A few years ago a cross-state bicycle tour passed through the Center. As interesting as looping around the Center was, the riders observed that nothing about the vaguely industrial site fit the conventional stereotypes of what high tech looks like. NASA Langley does not fit many stereotypes. It takes a close examination to discover the many ways it has contributed to the development of flight.

As part of the national celebrations commemorating the 100th anniversary of the Wright brothers' first flight, James Schultz, an experienced journalist with a gift for translating the language of engineers and scientists into prose that nonspecialists can comprehend, has revised and expanded *Winds of Change*, his wonderful guide to the Center. This revised book, *Crafting Flight*, invites you inside. You will read about one of the Nation's oldest research and development facilities, a place of imagination and ingenuity. If this is your first "visit," you will surely find many surprises. If you are a veteran, the pictures and text will evoke many memories.

For five years, I had the privilege of serving as the NASA Langley Visiting Historian. Like the other historians who have spent time at the Center, I have developed a keen appreciation for the work that has been done here. In April 2002, the Center invited me to participate in the ceremony celebrating the American Institute of Aeronautics and Astronautics' selection of Langley as a historic aerospace site. This is an international award that recognizes sites where significant contributions were made in aeronautics and astronautics.

Asked to give a speech, I spent considerable time reflecting on the importance of "community" to the development of technology, indeed, all of history. Technology is more than machines. It is, as the brilliant historian of technology Brooke Hindle once said: "making and doing." The "making and doing" of flight (atmospheric or space) has required an extraordinary community and Langley has been vital to the effort.

The speech I made on that occasion is reprinted in the following pages. I could not have been more thrilled to learn that it captured sentiments that resonated deeply with many individuals connected with the Center. It is an honor to have it become part of this book, just as it was to be associated with Langley for several years.

Deborah G. Douglas, Ph.D.
Curator of Science and Technology
MIT Museum, Cambridge, Massachusetts

Langley 8-Foot High-Speed Tunnel in 1936.

GRIN photo no. GPN-2000-001821

Langley 16-Foot High-Speed Tunnel in 1949.

GRIN photo no. GPN-2000-001931

A Boeing 777 semispan model in the NTF.

NASA Langley photo no. EL-2000-00153

STANDING ON THE SHOULDERS OF GIANTS

"If I see further, it is because I stand on the shoulders of giants," wrote Isaac Newton to Robert Hooke. Paraphrasing Newton a bit, if the American aerospace industry is to continue as the world leader, it will be because it stands on the shoulders of giants. So who were these "giants?" It is common practice among aviation history enthusiasts to point to individuals—Ludwig Prandtl, Theodore von Karman in the technical realm; Donald Douglas, William Boeing among many manufacturers; Hap Arnold, Billy Mitchell, William Moffett in the military; and Charles Lindbergh and Amelia Earhart among the scores of pilots—and surely individuals, especially these individuals, matter. The American Institute of Aeronautics and Astronautics is doing a daring thing then: it is honoring places.

I could not be more pleased because for the past five or six years I have had the privilege to "Think Langley, Work Langley, Dream Langley." (This is a variation on a quotation of Massachusetts Institute of Technology (MIT) president Richard C. Maclaurin, who led the campaign at the turn of the century to build our Cambridge campus and was describing to alumni how MIT had gotten into his system!) The Langley Memorial Aeronautical Laboratory (now the NASA Langley Research Center) is a remarkable place, a place that has consistently transformed mostly ordinary engineers and scientists into a premier technical community.

To be sure, Langley has had its share of "stars." Their names are well-known to you, but this plaque honors a community, the collective endeavors of individuals and a Nation. Years from now, when maybe the Center no longer exists, there will be this bronze plaque. Imagine in two or three centuries, stumbling across it in the woods among the ruins of buildings, much as we have stumbled across the last remnants of George Wythe's old homestead. Imagine asking yourself: "What was this place? What were they doing? How did this work change the world?" In your mind's eye, can you see the archeologist clutching a crumbling copy of *Engineer in Charge* or *Winds of Change*, exclaiming, "Here is where the 16-Foot Tunnel was!" "That's where the NTF [National Transonic Facility at Langley Research Center] stood!" "And look, the 8-Foot High Speed Tunnel is still standing!"

These archeological remnants will only tell a small part of the story, for this is a community far more vested in ideas. Few here today could tell you where the famous Propeller Research Tunnel (PRT) once stood, but most know the story of the NACA [National Advisory Committee for Aeronautics, NASA's predecessor] cowling. The PRT has been gone for decades, but you can (and people do) download copies of the NACA Technical Reports and Memoranda documenting the labors of many researchers in that place. Instinctively, then, you know that communities are more than instruments and tools. Great communities, you know, are places of intellectual opportunity.

Langley was established in 1917, meaning the cornerstone was laid and construction got underway. With only a little bit of cash, the new National Advisory Committee for Aeronautics played a tricky game of leveraging the resources of the military to build a laboratory. Aficionados of this history know this is a story of ups and downs, ambition and disappointment. Anyone who has started something new understands well the vertiginous arc of emotions unleashed as soon as the first pilings (real or metaphorical) start being pounded into the Earth. In 1920, three modest brick buildings nestled within a new Army Air Field were dedicated. Admiral David W. Taylor, the Navy's brilliant engineer,

Eight of the twelve members of the National Advisory Committee for Aeronautics attending the 9th Annual Aircraft Engineering Research Conference at Langley Field, Virginia, on May 23, 1934. Pictured from left to right are Charles Lindbergh; Vice Admiral Arthur Cook; Charles Abbot, Secretary of the Smithsonian; Dr. Joseph Ames, Committee Chairman; Orville Wright; Edward Warner; Fleet Admiral Ernest King; Eugene Vidal, Director Bureau of the Commerce.

GRIN photo no. GPN-2002-000024

Hanger construction at Langley in 1922.

GRIN photo no. GPN-2000-001378

Amelia Earhart, front center, at Langley in 1928. Engineer in Charge Henry J. E. Reid is to her right and Fred Weick is in back on right.

NASA Langley photo no. EL-1996-00230

declared, challenged, prophesied that the new Langley Memorial Laboratory would become a mecca for aeronautical engineers.

You had to be the hardy sort to make the pilgrimage in those first few years. To go to work at Langley in 1920 was reminiscent of the experiences of 19th century civil engineers assigned to remote locations with few amenities. While the NACA committee members spent time trying to figure out a way to move from Hampton back to Washington, D.C., the young men who were hired to work at Langley began to form a cohesive community.

They began by building a wind tunnel. Edward Warner, the new NACA Chief Physicist—he got that title so he did not have to take the Civil Service exam; engineers had to take the civil service exam and scientists did not—was fresh out of MIT. MIT had established the first aeronautical engineering program in the United States in 1913. It built its first "real" wind tunnel at this time—the hole cut by students in the side of a ventilation duct in the 1890s does not count as a "real" wind tunnel—based on plans given to Jerome Hunsaker during his visit to the National Physical Laboratory in England. MIT President Maclurian asked the NPL for these plans, and his good friend and former teacher, NPL Director Richard Glazebrook had complied. Warner, along with Donald Douglas, had been one of the most active in building MIT's tunnel. Now he was primed to do it again for the NACA.

Neither engineers nor historians have had many kind things to say about "Wind Tunnel No. 1." It certainly was not a source of new insights in the nascent field of aerodynamics, but it supplied a purpose and focal point for this early cadre of NACA employees. It also reinforced in the minds of these young American engineers that Europe had become the preeminent source of new ideas and research techniques in aeronautical engineering. If you don't believe me, check out the fact that many of the oldest publications now found in the Floyd L. Thompson Library (one of the world's best collections, by the way) are in languages other than English.

What an odd bunch these Langley engineers must have seemed. In the muggy, mosquitoey muck of newly drained swampland in the segregated south was this band of a dozen or so indefatigable young men who wanted to work all night. They hearkened from northern and midwestern colleges, read German and French journals and spoke in the opaque language of mathematics and technical terms. On one side of the field they watched the latest Army airplanes take off and land, and on the other, young African-American students from Hampton Institute [now Hampton University] farm agricultural plots by hand. "Interesting" can hardly have begun to describe the dynamics of this enterprise. Needless to say, they were a pretty cohesive and tough group when Max Munk arrived on the scene.

Max Munk was one of Ludwig Prandtl's star pupils, recruited by the NACA to replace Edward Warner, who wanted to return to MIT. Munk had earned two doctorates—one in engineering and one in physics—from Göttingen by 1917 at age 27. He was also of Jewish ancestry, which meant that in an environment of increasing anti-Semitism, he was more willing to consider leaving Germany and Prandtl was more willing to let him go. It would prove a critical hire for the NACA.

Assigned to the NACA office in Washington with the official job title "technical assistant"—this was due to anti-German sentiment and immigration restrictions after World War I—most of his work was on theoretical problems. But Munk was also the creative genius and designer of the Variable Density Tunnel (VDT) that began operations in 1922 and later the Propeller Research Tunnel. These two wind tunnels transformed the

Chief of Aerodynamics, Elton Miller, and Sperry M-1 in Propeller Research Tunnel in 1927.

NASA Langley photo no. EL-2000-00342

NACA cowling (covering over engine) #10 on an airplane in Propeller Research Tunnel in 1928.

NASA Langley photo no. EL-2000-00344

P-51 Mustang in the Full Scale Tunnel in 1945.

NASA Langley photo no. EL-2000-00363

Langley laboratory into a major research facility on par with the best in Europe. From the VDT came the series of reports presenting the NACA family of airfoils. From the PRT came the NACA cowling. Both accomplishments won considerable acclaim. But all was not well at Langley.

Essentially, Munk and the Langley engineers did not get along. Munk may have been brilliant, but he was not in charge of either Langley or the NACA. Needless to say, the Langley engineers chafed at the fiats he issued. He was outspoken and, on occasion, offensive. He drove the Langley engineers crazy. But the real issue was: What sort of laboratory was Langley to be? Munk wanted to replicate the German research university model. The Langley engineers believed they had a different mandate: to work collaboratively to find practical solutions to the problems of flight. Munk's resignation set the stage for a new period in the history of the Laboratory.

"Hurricanes Daily!" was the theme of an advertisement in a 1930 issue of the *Saturday Evening Post*. The hyperbole and emotional rhetoric of the ad would become commonplace for descriptions of the new NACA Full-Scale Tunnel (FST). The dedication of the FST in 1931 was supposed to be a modest affair, but neither the press nor the visiting engineers could contain themselves. Over the next decade, it became apparent that the FST would not achieve its research objective or the pioneering status that the VDT and PRT had. Yet, the facility's critical importance to the history of the NACA and Langley cannot be overstated. Engineers made great use of the FST, and it has proven invaluable over many decades for development studies.

The historic significance of the Full Scale Tunnel derives from its monstrous size and the tremendous emotional reaction that visitors experienced when seeing the tunnel for the first time. Ordinary people do not experience technology as intellectual abstractions. An airplane in flight is a "miracle" to be wondered at, not an assemblage of scientific puzzles like boundary layer theory. The vast scale of the FST conveyed the importance of long-term investment in research equipment, of institutional permanence and of aviation's prominent place in the life of the Nation. The public, if they knew what the initials NACA stood for—and most did not—saw the organization's mission to make airplanes fly faster, further, higher, and safer. In the FST, though the price tag was steep, they could easily apprehend the fact that the engineers at Langley were upholding the mandate. To the aeronautical engineering community, the FST communicated an additional and critical message. The message was not a didactic one but rather an invitation to the scores of engineers, who were largely untrained in higher mathematics and deeply skeptical of "theory," that these activities were vital to the disciplines future development.

The Langley engineers were inventing a hybrid practice that combined the theoretical and the practical. It should be noted that outsiders learned as much about "how" the Langley engineers undertook a project—the process—as they did from the research results. The lesson of the 1930s was that both research and development work were essential to the sustenance of a vital technical community. Lest one think this was an easy thing to do or that all was harmony, you need only recall the bitter rivalry between Eastman Jacobs and Theodore Theodoreson. It is very difficult to reconcile and manage competing modes of intellectual inquiry.

World War II brought the idea of "national service" to the fore. On the one hand, "national service" was the raison d'être of Langley, in particular its work for and with the military but the imperatives of war meant that research inquiries were largely terminated and the focus shifted almost completely to development projects. (The notable exception

Max Munk in his office at Langley in 1926.

NASA Langley photo no. EL-1997-00144

Electrical engineer Kitty Joyner at Langley in 1952.

NASA Langley photo no. EL-2000-399

Langley staff working on IBM type T04 electronic data processing machine in 1957.

NASA Langley photo no. EL-2000-404

to this was the aircraft structures group led by Eugene Lundquist and Paul Kuhn who deliberately designed building 1148 to be too small to do the Army Air Force's static loads testing work and therefore maintained an emphasis on research.) The war work had its gratifications and rewards, but it also brought significant change.

Langley was suddenly a much larger facility. There were multiple research groups each with their own specialized tunnel or laboratory. There were many more people (growing from 500 to 3,200 in five years) including, for the first time, a significant number of women working in professional positions. Langley was not only the center of its employees' work lives, but also their social lives. From sports to Sunday School, Langley people (then as now) tended to hang out with each other. Locals dubbed them "NACA Nuts," although the relationship of Langley to Hampton Roads is basically the same as "town-gown" relationships everywhere.

The establishment of Lewis (now Glenn) and Ames laboratories meant that Langley was now one of three NACA facilities. To ensure success and continuity, several of Langley's best and most entrepreneurial engineers went west to organize, direct, and staff these new labs. This resulted in yet another substantive change wrought during the World War II period: the creation of competition (for resources and ideas) within the NACA. It would prove a key change for Langley in the postwar period.

The period stretching from the end of World War II to 1957 should probably be called aviation's "Second Golden Age." For those of you who worked at Langley during this time: Can you imagine a more productive, interesting, challenging, exhilarating (and perhaps exhausting) time? The aerospace industry (along with the electronics and chemical industries) could not grow fast enough as Americans invested generously in science and technology. The turbojet revolution supplied an astonishing new research agenda. The story of Richard Whitcomb's discovery of the area rule has been well-told, but less well-known is the fact the Langley performance tests of the NACA 65-Series airfoils were the basis for the design method that the NACA presented in a series of three confidential memorandums known as "The Compressor Bible." This was work critical to the development of the turbofan.

Or, what about the astonishing aircraft structural mechanics group, widely hailed for its "ability to attract bright young university graduates... [and] develop them into first-class research men?" Like most Langley engineers, "Lundquist's Lions" as they were known, worked in large unpartitioned rooms with shared double desks. There was a single telephone. Your computer wore a skirt (and like now, had the powerful potential to distract). Your first assignment was to read and master the main works of Stephen Timoshenko. Then you'd get a problem. The real test was your ability to develop a project, conduct it, analyze the results, and write a report fit to publish. To keep you sharp, there were weekly seminars (works in progress talks) by your colleagues. Lundquist would let you take time off to go to graduate school if you showed exceptional promise, but he also was one of the chief advocates for having graduate courses taught at Langley.

And then the Soviet Union launched a 23-inch sphere into orbit on Oct. 4, 1957. Sputnik precipitated a national reaction not unlike that following Sept. 11, 2001; it also brought a close to the NACA. Dr. James Hansen has characterized the next two decades as Langley's "spaceflight revolution." The transformation manifests itself in many ways, but most significantly Langley went from being a self-contained research laboratory to an integrated national research center. The goal of research was less one of discovery and more one of facilitating the formation of a national agenda in aeronautics and space research. As former NASA Administrator Robert Seamans put it during his 1999 speech at

Langley's 737 flying laboratory flight tested advanced warning wind shear detectors to make aircraft safer.

NASA Langley photo no. EL-1996-00019

Cockpit of Shuttle *Atlantis* showing multifunction electronic display system.

NASA Langley photo no. EL-2000-00036

Proteus aircraft lands after collecting data for a cirrus cloud study.

Langley Office of External Affairs photo archives

Langley: "The goal was to do enough research to enable NASA to make independent judgments about the contracts it was letting." The military, he argued, had made the mistake of relying on outsiders (from the universities and industry) to evaluate work and formulate its agenda.

In this period, Langley also had to adapt to the mission model of research. Congress debated and funded specific missions with clear objectives: a crewed space program; a supersonic commercial transport; a mission to Mars. It is with the Viking Program and during the tenure of Center Director Ed Cortright that it became clear that the "spaceflight revolution" (the transformation from NACA to NASA) was now complete.

The period that followed—from the mid-1970s to the end of the Cold War—was marked by the reexamination of the role of aeronautics research. One of the more ambitious efforts was design and construction of the National Transonic Facility at Langley. What is obvious, however is that some of the greatest successes have been unanticipated by many outside the NASA family. Researchers in the Transonic Dynamics Branch have always known they work in a unique facility, but it has taken much longer for the rest of the world to recognize that fact. Likewise NASTRAN, a computer software program, is a major albeit unheralded accomplishment.

Until the early 1990s, the military was a reliable patron. With the end of the Cold War, there was the painful reality of downsizing. There were many who were asking: "What is the "return on investment" we get for a Langley? Why should we continue to spend on this work?" Langley managers took the questions to heart and carefully examined research goals. There was an unprecedented quest for efficiency, while maintaining research integrity within NASA as a whole. Revising organizational structure was the focus of innovative energy, as well as an emphasis on new forms of outreach.

But what of the future? Alfred Chandler wrote in his Pulitzer Prize-winning history, *The Visible Hand: The Rise of the Modern Business Enterprise* that it was revolutions in transportation and communication technology—specifically the railroad and the telegraph—that provided the foundation for not only the rise of the modern business enterprise but also the national economy that transformed the United States into a world power. It is not a particularly bold observation then, to suggest that aerospace and the Internet are the technologies key to a global economy.

Does Langley matter? I believe it does. Competition is not only beneficial in the marketplace of goods but also in the marketplace of ideas. As industries go, aerospace does not require much in the way of materials. The real expense in aerospace is human resources. There are not many pounds of aluminum in even the largest of aircraft or spacecraft, but the human effort required to design, construct, and operate an air transportation system or a satellite communication system is immense.

Where are the "idea mines" that the Nation's aviation and space enterprises will tap in order to maintain their productivity? What organizations have the intellectual venture capital to formulate and evaluate a national research agenda in aerospace? What entities have the wherewithal to sustain investment in studies that supply the broad global data sets that help our Nation understand the world we inhabit? Where is cutting edge research best pursued? Industry? University? Government?

Viking aeroshell in a Langley lab in 1973.
NASA Langley photo no. EL-2000-00454

High-wing model tested in the NTF at Langley.
Langley Office of External Affairs photo archives

Inflatable space structures display in building 1148, Structures and Materials Lab during the 2001 Open House.
NASA Langley photo no. EL-2001-00202

The answer is all of the above. We need different types of facilities, different communities, because there is no "one best way" or "one best organization" to solve all of the problems in aerospace. The strength of this community has been its diversity and the stimulation supplied by the intersection of strikingly different thought styles. Langley has been less about boldness, more about breadth and depth of knowledge.

Naturally, I will hedge my bets a bit here, as after all, I'm a historian, not a fortune-teller. But to my mind, Langley has been among the giants whose broad shoulders have helped support the Nation's aviation and space enterprises. The plaque unveiled today reminds us of what has been achieved. It is a splendid and well-deserved tribute. May the vision and hard work of your predecessors also be an inspiration as you face the challenges—for surely there are many—in the days to come. May you continue to be both mecca and mine for those who wish to reshape the world of aeronautics and space.

Simplified drawing based on da Vinci
lifting airscrew design.

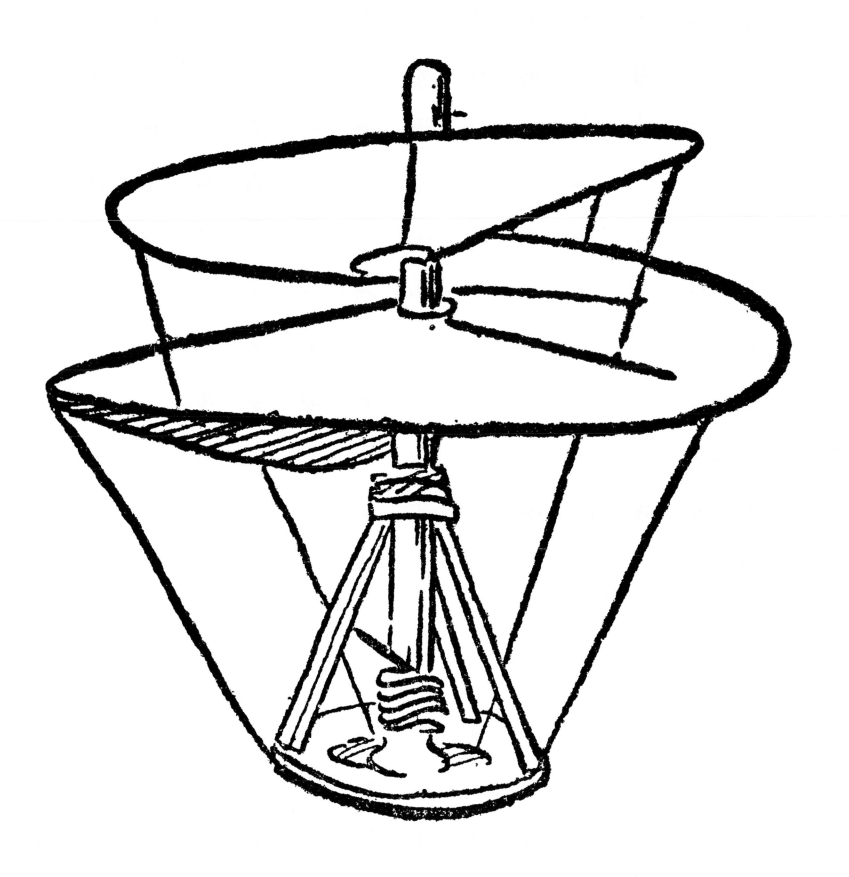

1

CRAVING FLIGHT

In the latter part of the 15th century, Leonardo da Vinci spent many of his waking hours attempting to perfect an "ornitottero," or ornithopter, a helicopter-like craft whose primary mechanism was a spiral airscrew built to obtain lift. He was convinced that avian anatomy proved beyond doubt that human flight would be no more and no less a matter of mastering essential mathematical principles. Da Vinci wrote, notes biographer Serge Bramly, that a bird "is an instrument functioning according to mathematical laws, and man has the power to reproduce an instrument like this with all its movements."[1]

So committed was da Vinci that by 1496 he began discrete, secret experiments with model craft from the heights of buildings near his workshop in Milan. Bramly believes that Leonardo based his research on documents such as those produced by medieval thinker Villard de Honnecourt, who made a detailed sketch of a bird beating its wings. On a reduced scale, owing to negligible weight and air resistance, small models could have worked in much the same way that toy gliders do today. Indeed, da Vinci likely began design experiments with "a little model made of paper, whose axis will be made of a fine steel blade, placed under strong torsion... when released, it will turn the helix." Even scaled up, weighted with a human-size (if lightweight) dummy, with spring-operated blades, and constructed of reeds and silk, the ornitottero should have been able to fly for a brief period.[2]

The problem of scaling up ornitottero design led Leonardo to study the relationship between birds' wing size and weight. He deduced there was no fixed rule; some large birds like the pelican have short wings relative to weight whereas a flying mammal like a bat has long wings relative to size. For the ornitottero, Leonardo therefore envisioned wings of different sizes that could be bent, stretched, and moved in such a way as to rise vertically and then fly horizontally. To that end, he sought out the lightest, strongest, and most supple materials then available: pinewood strengthened with lime, raw and sized silk, canvas covered with feathers; leather treated with alum or smeared with grease for lanyards and straps, young pine laths or reeds for the chassis, and steel and horn for the springs.[3]

Bramly writes that da Vinci was "full of faith," [spending]

endless hours on his invention. Others might have tried to fly before him, but no one had pursued this dream with such patience, ingenuity, daring and tenacity.

He must have given up in the end the idea of jumping from the roof [of a nearby building].... Perhaps he used the roof only to test the load his wings could bear, or try out his models. Prudently, he decided [writing in his journal] 'You will experiment with this machine over a lake and you will wear attached to belt a long wineskin, so that if you fall in, you will not be drowned.'

Bramly is not certain da Vinci attempted to fly, but thinks that he might have tried. It is likely that the end result would have been a kind of kite-like hang glider rather than an engine-containing chassis with mobile wings.[4]

Da Vinci was not the first would-be aviator. Nor, for 400 more years, would he be the last. Even though skeptics may have thought the skies would forever remain the domain of insects and birds, many pioneers were eager to take on the aerial challenge.

National Air and Space Museum, Smithsonian Institution, SI neg. no. A-46529-F

National Air and Space Museum, Smithsonian Institution, NASM videodisc no. ZB-41440

Nature served as a template and guide. Observers noted how leaves drifted from trees, clouds scooted across the skies, bubbles floated, and creatures without feathers, like bats, nimbly flew through air. Certain species of fish, squirrels, lemurs, lizards, even snakes glided and remained airborne for a few seconds. Animals living in water sometimes moved in ways reminiscent of flight, like whales and dolphins breaching and then, resubmerging, navigating like avian imports. There seemed abundant evidence that many creatures could escape Earth's surface, at least for a short time.[5]

People, of course, were distinctly unavian, with a strong, if heavy, skeleton, considerable musculature, water-containing inner organs, and a relatively weighty brain encased in thick bone. In contrast, a bird is born with honeycombed yet reinforced bones, huge (in relation to body weight) flight muscles, flexible wing arrangements, feathers that provide both lift and propulsion (and weatherproofing), as well as an oxygen-rich metabolism and anatomical structure uniquely suited to the physiological requirements of flight.[6]

Despite the obvious success of birds, many hopeful innovators would be bitterly disappointed by slavish devotion to the bird-like. One, described as the "Saracen of Constantinople," died in the 11th century while trying to fly with a stiffened cloak. Almost five hundred years later, in 1507, one Abbot Damina of Tungland was injured in an attempt to fly with cloth wings from the walls of Stirling Castle in Scotland.[7] Many others, their fates poorly or not at all recorded, would jump, flap, stall, and fall in vain attempts to wiggle out of grav-

ity's constant clutch. If humans were to fly, it seemed it would not be like birds.

PLYING THE OCEAN OF AIR

Early aviators struggled to understand the interaction of air with solids, like wood and textiles. Simple air resistance slows moving objects by imposing a force opposite to the motion. Air resistance increases with the square of speed, so that acceleration is slowed and the object eventually stops. Absent a continuing, accelerating force, even a rocket shot into the atmosphere will fall back to Earth, reaching a final speed known as terminal velocity. The atmosphere offers little resistance to a dense stone. On the other hand, a feather will fall more slowly because the shape of its surface creates much greater air resistance in proportion to its negligible weight. (In a vacuum, in a gravitational field, both stone and feather fall equally fast.)[8]

Lift is a more complex phenomenon. It is produced by the motion of specially shaped surfaces through the air and acts in a direction essentially perpendicular to the motion. Thus if a lift-generating body moves horizontally, its lift works to counteract gravity. Without any motive power or atmospheric effects, such as thermals (rising warm air currents), a body cannot produce enough lift to overcome gravity and stay aloft indefinitely. Lift slows descent and allows the body to follow a sloping path to the ground in the graceful action known as gliding.[9]

Nature exploits such forces in a variety of ways. Many plants extend their ranges by distributing seeds that mimic aerodynamic shapes. Some seeds have true wing shapes that generate lift, allowing them to glide great distances. Other seeds look like advanced designs for military aircraft, like the B-2 Stealth bomber. One, the maple seedpod, spins in autorotation like tiny helicopter blades as it descends, its wings generating lift that slows its fall and gives the wind time to carry the seed away from its parent.[10]

Innovators noted closely these phenomena and attempted a modest degree of aerodynamic experimentation. Prehistoric hunters not only took note of the ways their projectiles penetrated animal flesh, but also how straight and sure they flew. The tails of arrows contained feathers or feather substitutes such as leather, leaves, or fur to stabilize them in flight. Other hand-tossed devices, such as boomerangs and disks of wood and metal, could travel substantial distances and were used in hunting and during battle. In particular, boomerangs, often fashioned in the classic shape of the letter V, anticipated modern aerodynamic practice and design.

Kites also exploit the possibilities of flight. In producing fabric and paper prototypes, designers gleaned insight from the shape and movement of bird wings. Eventually tethered kites would be used in religious ceremonies, for war, and simply for entertainment. In China, records indicate that kites appeared 2,000 years ago and were used by the military to hoist sentries aloft to observe the movements of enemy troops. In Europe, the first known use of kites is recorded in a 14th century book in an account depicting bomb-carrying kites attacking a castle. Only much later did kites take on their modern identity as children's toys, although they were still employed in such diverse tasks as fishing

in hard-to-reach waters and experiments with electricity.[11]

Kites were prized for simplicity and dependability, both of which correlated directly to simple aerodynamic principles. They remain aloft because their surface area resists the wind. Held at an angle by string, the kite deflects moving air downward. In a breeze of constant strength, forces applied by the wind and the string are perfectly balanced, and the kite hangs nearly motionless in air.[12]

By the Middle Ages, two other aviation-like devices had been developed: the windmill, an early kind of propeller, and the model helicopter. Toys using the principle of the helicopter— a rotary blade turned by the pull of a string—were also widely known.

Some three centuries later, the first flights of human-carrying balloons occurred. The fact that warmed air rises and can be harnessed to lift weight occurred to French paper-maker Joseph Montgolfier one evening in 1783 as he watched the fire in his hearth. Montgolfier made a bag of fine silk and lit a fire under it. The bag filled and rose to the ceiling.

In June of that year, aided by his brother, Montgolfier demonstrated the effect in public by raising a huge cloth bag filled with the gaseous effluvia from burning wood and straw. When this primitive balloon actually proved workable, the brothers attached a basket and selected the world's first balloonists: a duck, a sheep, and a cockerel. The animals landed unharmed after an eight-minute voyage.

In November 1783, two human volunteers ascended in a Montgolfier

Paintings of balloon flights
in France.

National Air and Space Museum, Smithsonian Institution, SI neg. no. 71-309

National Air and Space Museum, Smithsonian Institution, NASM videodisc no. ZA-04222

balloon equipped with a brazier. The fledgling fliers took along a bucket of water and sponges in case the fire burned out of control, but the first crewed balloon ascent proceeded without incident. The balloon rose 500 feet and floated above Paris rooftops for 25 minutes.[13]

Even as the Montgolfier brothers were developing their balloons, another experimenter was working on a different approach to lighter-than-air flight. Professor Jacques A.C. Charles filled a small bag of rubberized silk with hydrogen, a gas only seven percent as heavy as air. Launched in Paris, it flew for about 45 minutes before coming down 15 miles away in the village of Gonesse. The balloon met an unfortunate end; pitchfork-wielding villagers tore it to shreds, convinced they were destroying an instrument of the devil. Undeterred, Charles built a larger human-carrying balloon, which he flew just a month after Montgolfier's flight. The public enthusiasm for ballooning grew, so that an estimated 400,000 people witnessed Charles' takeoff from the Tuileries Gardens. Charles lifted skyward with a friend for what proved to be a two-hour flight, borne away by a 28-foot-wide balloon quite similar to modern gas-filled designs.[14]

GOING AERIAL

Although 13th century English monk Roger Bacon appears to have first proposed the specifics of lighter-than-air and powered craft, English baronet Sir George Cayley is generally credited with creating the concept of the modern airplane, laying the foundations of aerodynamics in a series of published works between 1799 and 1809. Cayley

designed airplanes with rigid wings to provide lift and with separate propelling devices to provide thrust. Cayley demonstrated, both with models and with full-size gliders, the use of the inclined plane to provide lift, pitch, and roll stability; flight control by means of a single rudder-elevator unit mounted on a universal joint; streamlining; and other devices and practices.

Born in Scarborough, England, Cayley began designing experimental aircraft after observing birds in flight. His first aircraft was a type of kite fitted with a long stick and a movable tail. Encouraged by his success with this simple design, Cayley designed a larger aircraft with fixed wings. The essential form of the modern airplane, a rigid-wing structure driven by a separate power plant, first appeared in a design of Cayley's from 1799. By 1808 he had constructed a glider with a wing area of almost 300 square feet. In 1853 Cayley built a triplane glider (a glider with three horizontal wing structures) that carried his unwilling coachman 900 feet before crashing. It was the first recorded flight by a person in an aircraft.[15]

In 1809, Cayley published a paper, "On Aerial Navigation," that laid the basis for the study of aerodynamics. In subsequent designs and experiments, Cayley iterated many concepts familiar to students of the modern airplane. He demonstrated the use of inclined, fixed wings to provide lift and roll stability; the use of a rudder steering control; the concept of streamlining; and the idea of the helicopter, an aircraft in which the lift and thrust are provided by the same mechanism. Cayley correctly predicted that sustained flight would only occur

Sir George Cayley and his
early aircraft designs.

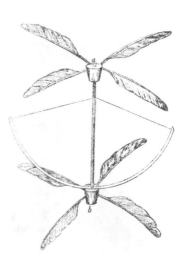

National Air and Space Museum, Smithsonian Institution, SI neg. no. 76-17422

Model of 1804 Cayley
glider.

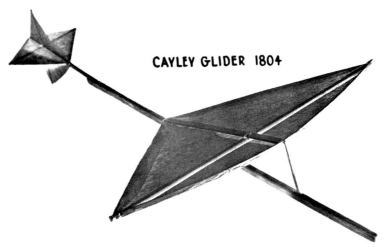

National Air and Space Museum, Smithsonian Institution, SI neg. no. 92-14967

Otto Lilienthal, c. 1890.

when a lightweight engine was developed to provide adequate thrust—an innovation finally accomplished by American aviators Orville and Wilbur Wright in 1903.[16]

Others would advance the fledgling science of aeronautics through the study of and experiments with gliding, thereby contributing extensively to the design of wings. These pioneers included the Frenchman Jean-Marie Le Bris, who tested a glider with movable wings, and the American John Joseph Montgomery. In 1843 British inventor William Samuel Henson published his patented design for an aerial steam carriage, a blueprint that did more than any other to establish the form of the modern airplane: a fixed-wing monoplane with propellers, fuselage, wheeled landing gear, and flight control by means of rear elevator and rudder. Steam-powered models made by Henson in 1847 were promising but unsuccessful. In 1890 French engineer Clément Ader built a steam-powered airplane and attempted the first actual flight of a piloted, heavier-than-air craft. However, the flight was not sustained, and the airplane brushed the ground over a distance of 160 feet. Inventors continued to pursue the dream of sustained flight.[17]

In the late 19th century, German Otto Lilienthal's experiments with aircraft, including kites and ornithopters, attained their greatest successes with glider flights. Lilienthal was captivated by the sweeping flight of seagulls he encountered while installing a foghorn of his own invention in German lighthouses. He studied birds in meticulous detail, eventually publishing an authoritative book drawing connections between natural and artificial flight. His aviation research was equally painstaking, begin-

National Air and Space Museum, Smithsonian Institution, SI neg. no. A-39013

National Air and Space Museum, Smithsonian Institution, SI neg. no. 85-18314

Lilienthal biplane glider in flight.

ning with a series of kite experiments in the 1870s and progressing to free-flying machines with wings modeled after those of soaring birds. In the course of five years in the 1890s, Lilienthal flew 18 different kinds of gliders, taking

Samuel Pierpont Langley, former secretary of the Smithsonian Institution and an avid aeronautical researcher.

NASA Langley photo no. 61L06095

careful notes on their aerodynamic qualities.[18]

He launched his flights from the top of a 50-foot hill that was built for the purpose in an open area near Berlin. The hill was conical, which allowed Lilienthal to fly directly into the wind no matter in which direction it blew, thus increasing the lift-generating movement of air over the curved, fabric-covered wings of his fixed-wing gliders. Half sitting on a trapeze so that his head and shoulders were above the wings, Lilienthal would step off the hill to begin a long, gentle glide to the ground. Maneuvering the craft by shifting his weight, the inventor regularly flew for distances up to 750 feet, thus becoming the first man to achieve sustained, controlled flight in a heavier-than-air machine.[19]

Lilienthal was piloting one of his most reliable gliders on a summer day in 1896 when a sudden gust of wind brought him to a standstill in midair. One wing lost its lifting power, dropped sharply, and the glider sideslipped to the ground. His spine broken in the crash, Lilienthal died the next day. Despite the tragedy, the body of aerodynamic data generated by his experiments would prove a crucial element in the development of powered flight.[20]

Beginning in 1896, the American civil engineer Octave Chanute had a limited success with multiplane gliders. But his most notable contribution to flight was his compilation of developments, *Progress in Flying Machines*, published in 1894. Additional information on aerodynamics and on flight stability was gained by a number of his experiments with kites. Before turning to aviation, Chanute built railroads and railroad bridges. Attracted by the work of Otto Lilienthal and other Europeans who were experimenting with gliding flight, Chanute (then in his sixties) established a glider camp on the sand dunes of Lake Michigan near Chicago. There, he and his associates made about 2,000 gliding flights without accident in machines of his own design. Chanute was particularly interested in problems of control and equilibrium, and the data he accumulated proved extremely useful to the Wright brothers in evolving their earlier designs. He was in constant correspondence with the Wrights and on several occasions visited Kitty Hawk, North Carolina, during the period of their gliding experiments, which preceded their successful powered flights.[21]

PRELUDE TO FLIGHT

One aeronautical pioneer who yearned to become the first to build a full-size, heavier-than-air flying machine was American inventor Samuel Pierpont Langley. Already a distinguished scientist by 1886, the year he began his aeronautical explorations in earnest, Langley was fascinated

Chanute biplane glider.

National Air and Space Museum, Smithsonian Institution, SI neg. no. A-30908-C

Chanute triplane glider under test by assistants in 1896.

National Air and Space Museum, Smithsonian Institution, SI neg. no. A-4387-C

Langley *Aerodrome 5* in 1895–96.

National Air and Space Museum, Smithsonian Institution, SI neg. no. 00165985 used with permission of *Popular Science* magazine

by the challenges flight presented. Despite criticisms from skeptical colleagues, and after 10 years of often frustrating struggle, Langley and his assistants were greatly encouraged by the successful launch of one of their uncrewed scale models on May 6, 1896.

Vowing to become the first to launch a full-scale, human-carrying airplane, the group intensified its efforts over the succeeding seven years. However, their final crewed test of Langley's *Aerodrome A* on December 8, 1903, ended abruptly in failure as the awkward machine lumbered not into the air, but into the chill waters of the Potomac River after being catapulted from its original position on top of a houseboat.

Writer Tom Crouch describes the preparation for the flight, as pilot Charles Manly "stripped off his outer clothes, [making] the flight clad in a cork-lined jacket, union suit, stockings and light shoes. Whether he succeeded or failed he faced a dunking in the icy waters of the Potomac and had no intention of being weighed down by heavy garments. The would-be aviator carefully picked his way through the jumble of bracing wires and took a seat in the flimsy cockpit. As Manly ran up the engine, Langley escorted his friends and guests back to the small boats so that they could either applaud a turning point in history or assist in Manly's rescue." Crouch describes what came next:

Satisfied with the sound of the engine and the operation of the controls, Manly gave the signal for release at about 4:45 p.m. He sped down the 60-foot track, felt a sharp jerk, and immediately found himself staring straight up at the sky as the machine flipped over onto its back and dropped into the water.

Manly hung from the cockpit sides and entered the water feet first. In spite of his precautions, he was trapped beneath the surface with his jacket caught on a metal fitting. Ripping the garment off, he struggled through the maze of broken wood and wire, only to reach the surface beneath an ice cake. Diving, he finally emerged in the open water some distance from the floating wreckage, just in time to see a concerned workman plunge under the remains of the craft to rescue him. Both men were quickly fished out of the water and carried to safety aboard the houseboat. Manly was uninjured, but so cold that Dr. F. S. Nash had to cut the clothes from his body.

Moments later, wrapped in a blanket and fortified with whiskey, this genteel son of a university professor startled the group by... delivering a "most voluble series of blasphemies." Samuel Pierpont Langley's 20-year quest for the flying machine was over.[22]

Nine days after Samuel Langley's hopes were doused in the Potomac, two bicycle-mechanic brothers from Dayton, Ohio, wrestled their prototype airplane into position on a desolate, windswept North Carolina beach. That they did succeed where others before had failed may have seemed almost miraculous at the time, but in retrospect owed much to a fortuitous combination of temperament, curiosity, ability, dogged perseverance, and a determined, systematic approach to engineering.

Langley Aerodrome houseboat on Potomac River.

NASA Langley photo no. 90L04341

Langley *Aerodrome A* catapulting off houseboat October 7, 1903.

National Air and Space Museum, Smithsonian Institution, SI neg. no. 85-18303

Langley *Aerodrome A* floating in Potomac River after launch on October 7, 1903.

National Air and Space Museum, Smithsonian Institution, SI neg. no. 93-245

BROTHERS EXTRAORDINAIRE

One cannot describe Wilbur and Orville Wright as mere tinkerers or run-of-the-mill bicycle mechanics. They were engineers of the first degree, who amplified one another's talents working side by side, forging a professional bond as strong as their personal bond. That affection would sometimes be tested as the brothers labored—first in Dayton, Ohio, and eventually on the windswept sands of Kitty Hawk, North Carolina—where they meticulously evaluated, designed, tested, redesigned, and then built a series of experimental aircraft that would culminate in a double-wing glider forever to be known as the Wright *Flyer*. That these two sons of a Midwestern cleric could, in a little over three years, accomplish what legions of others could not over the course of centuries came as no surprise to older Wright brother Wilbur. Biographer Tom Crouch, writing in *The Bishop's Boys*, cites Wilbur's words describing his relationship with sibling Orville:

> *From the time we were little children, my brother Orville and myself lived together, played together, worked together and, in fact, thought together. We usually owned all of our toys in common, talked over our thoughts and aspirations so that nearly everything that was done in our lives has been the result of conversations, suggestions and discussions between us.*[23]

Spurred by the 1896 death of glider pioneer Otto Lilienthal, Wilbur took the lead reading and learning about then-current research into the mysteries of flight. He quickly discovered one of the key problems—a wealth of misleading, inaccurate information:

> *Thousands of men had thought about flying machines and a few had even built machines which they called flying machines, but these were guilty of almost everything except flying. Thousands of pages had been written on the so-called science of flying, but for the most part the ideas set forth, like the designs for machines, were mere speculations and probably 90 percent [were] false. Consequently those who tried to study the science of aerodynamics knew not what to believe and what not to believe. Things which seemed reasonable were often found to be untrue, and things which seemed unreasonable were sometimes true. Under this condition of affairs students were accustomed to pay little attention to things they had not personally tested.*[24]

Crouch explains that Wilbur was careful in setting a goal and persistent in pursuing it:

> *He was the perfect engineer—isolating a basic problem, defining it in the most precise terms, and identifying the missing bits of information that would enable him to solve it. Other students of the subject lost themselves in a welter of confusing detail; they were lured into extraneous, if fascinating, blind alleys that led away from the basic problem. Not Wilbur. He had the capacity to recognize and the dogged determination required to cut straight to the heart of any matter.*[25]

Wilbur's talents were augmented by Orville's technical ingenuity and fastidiousness. Together, the brothers were unlike any individual or group that had taken up flight. Adding to their potential were family traits that could be traced to father Milton Wright, an iconoclastic

Orville (left) and Wilbur Wright,
c. 1910.

National Air and Space Museum, Smithsonian Institution, SI neg. no. 86-3026

bishop in the Church of the United Brethren in Christ. Like Milton, the brothers were independent thinkers with a deep confidence in their own talents, an unshakable faith in the soundness of their judgment, and a determination to persevere in the face of disappointment and adversity.[26]

Following their mother's death, Orville, who had spent several summers learning the printing trade, persuaded Wilbur to join him in establishing a print shop. In addition to printing services, the brothers edited and published two short-lived local newspapers. They also developed a local reputation for the quality of the presses that they designed, built, and sold to other printers. These printing presses were one of the first indications of the Wright brothers' extraordinary technical ability and their unique approach to the solution of problems in mechanical design.[27]

In 1892 the brothers opened a bicycle sales and repair shop where they began to build bicycles on a small scale in 1896. They developed a self-oiling bicycle wheel hub and installed a number of light machine tools in the shop. Profits from the print shop and the bicycle operation eventually went to fund the Wrights' aeronautical experiments from 1899 to 1905. In addition, the experience of designing and building lightweight, precision machines of wood, wire, and metal tubing was ideal preparation for the construction of flying machines.[28]

The brothers realized that a successful airplane would require wings to generate lift, a propulsion system to move it through the air, and a system to control the craft in flight. Otto Lilienthal, they reasoned, had built wings capable of carrying him in flight, while the builders of self-propelled vehicles were developing lighter and more powerful internal combustion engines. The final problem to be solved, they concluded, was that of control.[29]

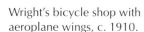

Wright's bicycle shop with aeroplane wings, c. 1910.

National Air and Space Museum, Smithsonian Institution, SI neg. no. A-31291

Most aeronautical experimenters up to that time sought to develop flying machines incorporating a measure of inherent stability. These aircraft tended to fly a straight and level course unless the pilot intervened to change altitude or direction. As experienced cyclists, the Wrights preferred to place complete control of their machine in the hands of the operator. Moreover, aware of the dangers of weight-shifting control (a means of controlling the aircraft by shifting the position of the pilot), the brothers were determined to direct their machine through a precise manipulation of the center of pressure on the wings. After considering various mechanical schemes for obtaining such control, they decided to try to induce a helical twist across the wings in either direction. The resulting increase in lift on one side and decrease on the other would enable the pilot to raise or lower either wing tip at will.[30]

Their first experiments with "wing warping," as the system would be called, were made with a small biplane kite flown in Dayton in the summer of 1899. Discovering that they could cause the kite to climb, dive, and bank to the right or left at will, the brothers began designing their first full-scale glider using Lilienthal's data to calculate the amount of wing surface area required to lift the estimated weight of both machine and pilot in a wind of given velocity.[31]

Realizing that Dayton, with its relatively low winds and flat terrain, was not the ideal place to conduct aeronautical experiments, the Wrights requested of the U.S. Weather Bureau a list of more suitable areas. In 1900, they selected Kitty Hawk, an isolated village on the Outer Banks of North Carolina, which offered high average winds, tall dunes from which to glide, and soft sand for landings. In October 1900, at Kitty Hawk, the Wrights tested their first glider, a biplane featuring 165 square feet of wing area and a forward elevator for pitch control. The glider developed less

Wright Brothers in hangar at Kitty Hawk.

National Air and Space Museum, Smithsonian Institution, SI neg. no. A-31205-B

Wright 1900 glider at Kitty Hawk. Noted on back of photo that glider did not fly.

National Air and Space Museum, Smithsonian Institution, SI neg. no. 89-4710

lift than expected, however, and very few free flights were made with a pilot on board. The brothers flew the glider as a kite, gathering information on the performance of the machine that would be critically important in the design of future aircraft.[32]

Eager to improve on this disappointing performance, the Wrights increased the wing area of their next machine to 290 square feet. Establishing their camp at the foot of Kill Devil Hills, four miles south of Kitty Hawk, the brothers completed 50 to 100 glides in July and August of 1901. As in 1900, Wilbur made all the glides, the best of which covered nearly 400 feet. The 1901 Wright aircraft was an improvement over its predecessor, but it still did not perform as well as their calculations had predicted. Moreover, the experience of 1901 suggested that the problems of control were not fully resolved.[33]

Realizing that the failure of their gliders to match calculated performance

was the result of errors in the experimental data published by their predecessors, the Wrights constructed a small wind tunnel with which to gather their own information on the behavior in an air stream of model wings of various shapes and sizes. The brilliance of the Wright brothers and their ability to visualize the behavior of a machine that had yet to be constructed was seldom more apparent than in the design of their wind tunnel balances, the instruments mounted inside the tunnel that actually measured the forces operating on the model wings. During the fall and early winter of 1901, the Wrights evaluated as many as 200 wing designs in their wind tunnel and gathered information on the relative efficiencies of various airfoils. They determined the effects of different biplane wing shapes, tip designs, and biplane gap sizes.[34]

With the results of the wind tunnel tests in hand, the brothers began work on their third full-scale glider. They tested

Wright 1903 Flyer on
ground at Kitty Hawk.

National Air and Space Museum, Smithsonian Institution, SI neg. no. 93-12785

the machine at the Kill Devil Hills camp in September and October 1902. It performed exactly as the design calculations predicted. For the first time the brothers shared flying duties, completing hundreds of flights that covered distances in excess of 600 feet and remaining in the air for as long as 26 seconds. In addition to gaining significant flight experience, the Wrights were able to complete their control system by adding a movable rudder linked to their helical wing-warping system.[35]

With the major aerodynamic and control problems behind them, the brothers pressed forward with the construction of their first powered machine. They designed and built a four-cylinder internal combustion engine with the assistance of Charles Taylor, a machinist whom they employed in the bicycle shop. Recognizing that propeller blades could be understood as rotary wings, the Wrights were able to design twin pusher

propellers from data derived from a small wind tunnel they custom-built.[36]

Returning to their camp near Kill Devil Hills in September 1903, the brothers spent the next seven weeks assembling, testing, and repairing their powered machine, and conducting new flight tests with the 1902 glider. Wilbur made the first attempt at powered flight on December 14, but he stalled the aircraft on takeoff and damaged the forward section of the machine. Three days were spent making repairs and waiting for the return of good weather.[37] Biographer Tom Crouch describes the final steps leading to the second try:

[The brothers] were up and about early on the morning of December 17. The day dawned cold and clear. A frigid 24-mile-per-hour wind swept out of the north, freezing the pools of standing water that had collected in the sand hollows. The Wrights were accustomed to the cold.... The morning began with a familiar round of chores. While one man

Wilbur Wright watches his airborne
brother Orville make history
on December 17, 1903.

Langley Office of External Affairs photo archives

washed and shaved, the other fed chunks of driftwood into the makeshift stove that doubled for heating and cooking. Within half an hour both were dressed in white shirts, celluloid collars and ties....

By 10:30 the machine was set up at the head of the launch rail. A few drops of gasoline were pumped into each [engine] cylinder; the battery box was hoisted onto the wing and attached to the engine. After a final check all around, Wilbur and Orville walked to the rear and pulled the propellers through in unison. The engine coughed to life... They shook hands and Orv[ille] climbed into place beside the engine, prone on the lower wing with his feet braced against a board tacked to the rear spar....

At about 10:35, Orv shifted the [control] lever to the left. Slowly... the machine began to move down the rail into the teeth of a wind that was now gusting up to 27 miles per hour. Wilbur had no trouble keeping up with the craft, which rose from the track after only a 40-foot run....

It was over very quickly. The airplane floundered forward, rising and falling for 12 seconds until it struck the sand only 120 feet from the point at which it left the rail. You could have thrown a ball farther, but, for the Wrights, it was enough. For the first time in history, an airplane had taken off, moved forward under its own power, and landed at a point at least as high as that from which it had started—all under the complete control of the pilot. On this isolated, windswept beach, a man had flown.[38]

News of the Wrights' achievement was met with disbelief in the several years following their initial flights. The straitlaced brothers believed they should be taken at their word; they limited access to the details of their invention and permitted but a handful of individuals to witness a small number of test flights. By 1908, however, demonstration flights in France led to worldwide acclaim for the pair. In aeronautical circles it was assumed that the age of flight had finally arrived. But in the United States at least, flight continued to be regarded as an indulgence fit for adventurers, daredevils, and eccentrics. Even though the first transcontinental flight had taken place by 1911, the prospect of fleets of airplanes carrying paying passengers seemed, to put it mildly, improbable. In the first full decade of the 20th century, Americans of serious temperament dismissed the airplane as a fad or as a specialized machine suitable only for military purposes.[39]

Meanwhile across the Atlantic, Europe was well ahead of the United States in aeronautics. In Europe, governments were funding ambitious aeronautical research programs and private firms were designing new generations of airplanes. Americans of vision were convinced that aviation had a grand future and fretted over their country's seeming indifference to federally funded aeronautics research. By 1915, however, the jolt of World War I tumbled the Nation out of its aviation research slumber. In coming decades, the Wrights' legacy would be clear and irrefutable, as fleets of airplanes took to the air in times of peace and war.

Metal workers welding pipe in 1929.

2

A LABORATORY FOR FLIGHT

When just a young man, novelist Thomas Wolfe set out to see the world. His travels

eventually led him to the Virginia port city of Norfolk and, after he heard of work available

nearby, onward to the fishing hamlet of Hampton. There in the summer of 1918, Wolfe and

hundreds of others labored in the oppressive heat and humidity to construct a "flying

field." In his fictional, semiautobiographical book *Look Homeward, Angel*, Wolfe's alter

ego, Eugene Gant, recalls the experience as "the weary and fruitless labor of a nightmare."

The workers, wrote Wolfe, reshaped the landscape by blasting ragged stumps from spongy

soil and filling the resulting craters that "drank their shoveled toil without end," as they

graded and leveled the ground from dawn to dusk. Meanwhile, overhead, the "bird-men

filled the blue Virginia weather with the great drone of the Liberties," practicing aerial

observation and photography in British-designed and American-made de Havilland

DH-4s.

All the hard work had a dual purpose: the creation of a new U.S. Army Air Service

airfield and the Nation's first government-sponsored civilian aeronautical research labora-

tory. Both were named in honor of Samuel Pierpont Langley, former secretary of the

Smithsonian Institution and an avid aeronautical researcher. The research laboratory—

Langley Memorial Aeronautical Laboratory—would be overseen by a parent agency,

the National Advisory Committee for Aeronautics, or the NACA. The NACA's

Former Langley Director
Paul F. Holloway.

NASA Langley photo no. EL-2001-00434

Former Langley Research
Center Director Richard H.
Petersen next to a model of
the Pathfinder transport in
the National Transonic
Facility.

NASA Langley photo no. EL-2001-00410

The NACA Langley Laboratory would become one of the country's foremost sources for reliable, detailed information on aircraft design and performance. Aspiring aeronautical engineers attending universities read research papers published by Langley researchers. Both the fledgling commercial aircraft industry and those concerned with the performance of military aircraft looked to Langley for help with all manner of difficulties, from aerodynamic stability and control to structural integrity, from propulsion efficiency to means of reducing drag. As it tackled and solved a variety of problems related to airplanes and flight, Langley established an international reputation as the world's premier aeronautical laboratory by paying close attention to detail and displaying a passion for accuracy.[2]

The Laboratory enlarged its mission in the late 1950s when the arrival of the space age shook the international geopolitical order and promised dramatic new technological possibilities on the "high frontier." A successor agency, the National Aeronautics and Space Administration, or NASA, assumed responsibility for Langley, which was subsequently renamed Langley Research Center. NASA's mission, like the NACA's, was still geared to aeronautical research, but the new agency's mandate also commanded it to look beyond Earth's atmosphere and to create human-carrying craft that could navigate the unforgiving vacuum of space. "Langley led the way in aeronautical research in the first half of the 20th century," contends former Langley Director Paul F. Holloway (1991–1997), "and in the following decades we would also lead the way in aerospace-related engineering

straightforward mandate was to undertake "the scientific study of the problems of flight with a view toward their practical solution." The new organization would bring together the best of the public and private sectors by creating industry and government partnerships that would, in decades to come, advance American aviation far beyond its modest beginnings.[1]

science. In particular, Langley provided NASA with a large part of the engineering and administrative nucleus for the U.S. manned spaceflight program."

According to former Langley Director Richard H. Petersen (1985–1991), Langley was able to vault the United States into a preeminent position, first in aeronautical technology from 1920 through 1940, and next into then-emerging fields of aerospace science and engineering. "Langley also had a major responsibility in bringing the U.S. into the space era," Petersen says. "Project Mercury came out of Langley and much of the Apollo technology came from Langley. Langley people were also involved in the early Space Shuttle conceptual design. Langley was able to assemble a group of outstanding researchers on the cutting edge of their respective fields and technologies."

Throughout its history, with research and applied engineering, the Center has been responsible for some of the 20th century's fundamental aeronautical and aerospace breakthroughs. The Nation's first streamlined aircraft engine cowling was developed at Langley Laboratory. Among other firsts: the tricycle landing gear; techniques involving low drag-producing flush riveting; development of the sweptback wing; research that aided in breaking the sound barrier; the genesis and design of the Mercury space program; development of rendezvous and docking devices and techniques that made possible the Apollo Moon landing; and the design of other unique spacecraft, including a low-cost orbital space-science laboratory known as the Long Duration Exposure Facility, or LDEF.

NASA Langley photo no. EL-2000-00287

Prototypes of Mercury capsules were assembled by Langley technicians.

NASA Langley photo no. EL-1999-00386

Gemini Rendezvous and Docking Simulator suspended from the Langley Hangar.

NASA Langley photo no. EL-2000-00035

Model of the Hyper-X/Pegasus launch vehicle in the 31-Inch Mach 19 Tunnel.

The Space Shuttle *Challenger* deploys the Long Duration Exposure Facility in 1984. Mexico's Baja peninsula is visible to the upper left of the cargo bay.

NASA Langley photo no. EL-2001-00431

Langley staff theoretically analyzed the flight limiting problems of flutter and rotary wing mechanical instability and verified the theories by tests of scaled aeroelastic models in the 1930s and 1940s.

In addition, Langley developed and refined instrumentation systems for aircraft, contributed to improvements in aircraft structures and materials, and increased the understanding of structural dynamics and crashworthiness. Langley played a primary role in the development of generations of military and civil fixed and rotary wing aircraft.[3]

On March 3, 1915, the 63rd Congress passed a resolution authorizing the creation of a government-sponsored committee to study aeronautics. Thus the National Advisory Committee for Aeronautics was created and given $5,000 to begin aeronautical research. The NACA was composed of a Main Committee consisting of seven government and five private-sector members. The Committee was to meet in Washington, D.C., semi-annually (more often if necessary) to identify key research problems to be tackled by the agency and to facilitate the exchange of information within the American aeronautical community. The unsalaried Committee, independent of any other government agency, would report directly to the President, who appointed its constituent members. Perhaps too idealistically, it was hoped that members of the Committee would put ego, personal and public agendas, and personality conflicts aside in the interest of advancing aeronautical research. Considering human nature and the inherent limitations of working in committee, the

NASA Langley photo no. EL-1996-00158

The members of the Main Committee of NACA, which met in Washington, D.C. on April 18, 1929, include from left to right: John F. Victory, secretary; Dr. William F. Durand; Dr. Orville Wright; Dr. George K. Burgess; Brig. Gen. William E. Gillmore; Maj. Gen. James E. Fechet; Dr. Joseph S. Ames, Chairman; Rear Adm. David W. Taylor, USN (Ret.), Vice Chairman; Capt. Emory S. Land; Rear Adm. William A.Moffett; Dr. Samuel W. Stratton; Dr. George W. Lewis, director of aeronautical research; and Dr. Charles F. Marvin.

NACA Main Committee functioned surprisingly well.[4]

Beginning in 1920, upon his NACA appointment by President Woodrow Wilson, Wright brother Orville took his responsibilities seriously as a Main Committee member. According to biographer Tom Crouch, Orville remained a member of the NACA longer than anyone else in the history of the committee, until his death from a heart attack, on January 30, 1948, at the age of 77. Although, as Crouch notes, while Orville's

record of attendance at the annual and semiannual meetings over a period of 28 years was exemplary, yet his personal contributions had no special impact on the NACA program. He concentrated on those issues of greatest interest to him, such as championing the cause of the small investors who wrote in search of advice or assistance. He partic-

ipated in discussions but rarely exercised leadership.[5]

As the NACA began its work in Washington, high on the agenda was finding land on which to build its first research laboratory. The Committee's best chance to quickly obtain the required parcel was to cooperate with the Army Air Service, which was looking for a site to house an experimental facility with adjacent airfield. The land chosen was 1,650 acres just north of the small Virginia town of Hampton. At the time, the site was located in Elizabeth City County, a largely rural area that was home mostly to fishermen and farmers. The land was flat, fronting on water, which was advantageous when conducting test flights. It was east of the Mississippi and south of the Mason-Dixon line, an area generally prone to good weather and therefore good flying. It was no farther than 12 hours by train

Engineer David L. Bacon and physicist Frederick H. Norton escorted Orville Wright, in hat, around the laboratory during his visit in July 1922. To the right is George Lewis.

NASA Langley photo no. EL-1997-00137

from Washington, D.C. Nor was it so close to an unprotected coastal area as to be subject to attack or possible capture in the event of war.[6]

Although the first NACA laboratory building was complete by the end of the summer of 1917, the Army's resistance to a permanent civilian aeronautical laboratory (the Army felt the military would do a better job of airplane research than civilians) slowed the NACA research timetable. Matters were finally resolved, however, and on June 11, 1920, Langley Memorial Aeronautical Laboratory—and its first wind tunnel, appropriately christened "Wind Tunnel Number One"—was formally dedicated.[7]

In a speech delivered before the Air Force Association in Spokane, Washington, on May 31, 1957, NACA Executive Secretary John F. Victory framed the challenges confronting the organization in its early years: "Forty years ago we had just entered World War I and had a great deal to learn. We had but small knowledge of aeronautics—and most of that had come from abroad. We were short of spruce with which we then built planes; short of linen to cover the wings; short on engine power—we had no engine over 80 horse-power. We were short of factories, short of pilots, short of know-how. In short, we were just caught short."[8]

To confront the daunting technological challenges it faced, Langley Laboratory had to build a professional and support staff from the ground up. Early on, the NACA committed itself to finding the best and brightest to solve the problems of flight. Langley's people would matter most as the Laboratory pushed across the uncharted frontiers of aeronautical research.

Langley Memorial Aeronautical Laboratory as it appeared in 1918.

NASA Langley photo no. EL-2001-00419

The NACA hangars in 1931.

NASA Langley photo no. EL-2000-00354

A COLLECTIVE EFFORT

The young engineers who came to work at Langley in its first decades brought with them a particular sense of mission. Most were aeronautics enthusiasts, interested in all things with wings, rotors, and propellers. In coming to the Laboratory, these aeronautical engineers had not chosen a job, but a vocation. Some approached their labors with an almost religious intensity, working nights and weekends with a zeal of which only devotees are capable. The majority kept regular hours, but were no less enamored with the cause. For many, Langley was a dream come true: here was a one-of-a-kind research facility where the sky was literally the limit. "No one else in the country was doing this kind of work. It was so exciting it was unbelievable," says Axel T. Mattson, who arrived at Langley in 1941 and in 1974 retired from the

Center as assistant director for External Affairs.

Key to Langley's research strength was an atmosphere that fostered exploration and initiative. Individuals were encouraged to find out what worked. If a device, modification, or process was successful, it could then be incorporated onto an aircraft for testing and verification. If, on the other hand, an idea had merit but its application was faulty or incomplete, then the originators went back to the drawing board to incorporate lessons learned and prepared for another try. For the newly minted college graduate ready to make a permanent mark upon the world, Langley's greatest gift was the permission to try and try again until the mission was successful. Learning by repeated attempts may appear cumbersome, but failures indicated areas where further research was needed to improve the understanding of flight phenomena. At Langley, the mistakes were just as important as the successes, for they sowed the seeds of future accomplishment.[9]

"Hired fresh out of school with a minimum knowledge of aerodynamics and little practical experience of any kind, the majority of these early Langley researchers learned nearly everything on the job," writes *Engineer In Charge* author James Hansen. "Because they were so young, they had not learned that a lot of things could not be done, so they went ahead and did them."

No matter how much latitude Langley's staff was given, when all was said and done, applied engineering was what the Laboratory was about. But researchers did not simply slap parts together to see what worked. The Langley way was one of systematic parameter modification: that is, meticulous, exacting variation of one component, then another, and so on until the optimum configuration was achieved. Such a process took time, patience, and cooperation above all else. At Langley, no researcher ever really worked alone. Successful application of aeronautical research demanded collaboration.

Theoreticians were essential members of the Langley staff. The task of these individuals was to chip away at the physics of flight with the precise, unforgiving chisel of mathematics to explain and enlarge upon the results obtained in wind tunnels and in test flights. In the event that experimental results did not agree with theory, either the experiment was repeated or the theoreticians formulated new laws to explain the unexpected phenomena. But Langley theoreticians did more than scribble complex equations in notebooks. Their calculations led

Making test models in the 1930s.

NASA Langley photo no. EL-2001-00367

Designed to fly at very low airspeeds, this Custer channel wing aircraft never made it in to full production.

NASA Langley photo no. EL-2001-00475

Two mechanics measure and record wing ordinates on a Curtiss Jenny airplane.

NASA Langley photo no. EL-2001-00374

Model of a possible supersonic transport mounted in a wind tunnel.

NASA Langley photo no. EL-2001-00405

Scale model of an SBN-1 airplane in the 12-Foot Free Flight Tunnel in 1940.

NASA Langley photo no. EL-2000-00202

Vari-Eze designed by Burt Rutan in wind tunnel.

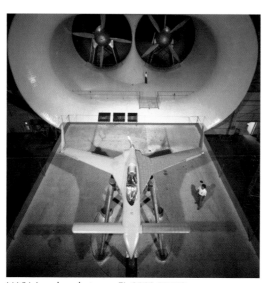

NASA Langley photo no. EL-2000-00463

to the design of thinner and lower drag wings, sturdier aircraft structures, better propellers, and the first widely used airplane deicing system, which put engine exhaust heat to good use.[10]

For their part, Langley engineers first used wood, then metal and composites, to model new aircraft designs. Laboratory researchers refined existing flight systems, improved engines, and reworked original aerodynamic shapes. Because many of Langley's most talented engineers came to the Laboratory with little or no background in theoretical studies, it took a while for them to learn how to use theory to enlarge upon or improve a given engineering approach. Nevertheless, some of Langley's best work was done by those very engineers who managed to relate abstract theory to pragmatic aeronautical requirements to arrive at new techniques or better devices.[11]

An expert support staff was also critical to Langley's ability to innovate. One of the most important factors considered by the Army and the NACA in site selection was the local availability of mechanics and technicians. Within an hour's car drive of Hampton there were numbers of workers skilled in wood, metal, and concrete construction; in marine and automobile repair; in toolmaking; and in the operation of electrical machinery. The Langley professional staff prized such craftsmen because they provided the essential support services on which all NACA research programs depended. Without such prized workers, research models could not have been made, wind tunnels could not have been built or properly maintained, and efficient daily operation would have proven impossible.[12]

The coalition of these groups, each with its own emphasis and strength, drove Langley to research excellence. Those who went to the Laboratory for assistance were impressed by the staff's abilities and were confident of receiving the best possible help. Said former McDonnell Douglas Corporation official L. Eugene Root, when interviewed by historian Michael Keller in the 1960s, "If you think the young guys at the NACA [could not make] your design... better, why, you have another think coming.... No one company, or one individual, could have ever gotten it together [or] the facilities that were required to make the United States of America tops aeronautically. It would never have happened if it had not been for the wisdom of putting together these laboratories and giving young, driving, ambitious and damn smart... young men a place to be, a place to go and something important to do that was really fundamental to the country."

As intellectually nimble and technically shrewd were the Langley staff, they nonetheless needed first-rate laboratories and wind tunnel facilities in which to do first-rate work. Langley's physical infrastructure would prove second to none.

HAVING THE RIGHT TOOLS

In 1901, to gather additional information on the performance of wing shapes, the Wright brothers built their first wind tunnel. It was a smallish wooden box that was six feet long and powered by a two-bladed fan. The Wrights were not the first to use wind tunnels in aerodynamic research—Briton Frank H. Wenham is generally considered to have originated the wind tunnel in 1871—but their use of the device was central to the refinement and, subsequently, to the success of their *Flyer*. It was cheaper, safer, and parameters could be easily varied without having to build full-scale models.[13]

In their simplest form, wind tunnels consist of an enclosed passageway—hence the term "tunnel"—through which air is pushed by one or more fans. Depending upon design, and whether outside air or another gas is used, the gas flowing through wind tunnels has certain properties of velocity, density, and temperature. To mimic in-flight conditions and monitor a wide range of an aircraft's physical reactions to those conditions, researchers mount instrumented models (or in certain instances, full-size craft) in the wind tunnel's heart, the test section. There, air or gas is made to flow around the (usually) stationary model. Many Langley tunnels took their names from the size of test sections.

Throughout its history, Langley has taken pride in an extensive wind tunnel complex, one of the largest of its kind in the world. Simply put, Langley wind tunnels have been one of the key elements of the Center's aerospace research program. There are specialized wind tunnels dedicated to a narrow range of investigations, and wind tunnels in which a wide variety of experiments are conducted. Langley wind tunnels are small and large; they are run at low, high, and ambient temperatures. Some operate at many times normal atmospheric pressure; others, at fractions of an atmosphere.

Models and shapes of airplanes, helicopters, airplane wings, rotors, dirigibles, pontoons, submarines, satellites,

A technician unlatches a door in the guide vanes of the 16-Foot Transonic Tunnel.

NASA Langley photo no. EL-1996-00006

and spacecraft have all been evaluated in Center tunnels. Langley wind tunnels are also durable, so much so that a handful remain from the Laboratory's earliest days, even if in substantially renovated form.

Today, Langley Research Center continues to upgrade and improve its wind tunnel complex. Over the years, though, money has not always been readily available when the time came to renovate or replace tunnels. As it does today for NASA, the U.S. Congress held the purse strings for the NACA and carefully considered every request for new facilities. NACA officials appearing before Congressional committees were adept at explaining why funds were needed and exactly how the money would be spent. Still, being regularly grilled by committee was not something any NACA official relished. Nor did Congress routinely write the NACA a blank check for projects. Some projects were delayed, some denied outright. But there were ways to get around budget restrictions, as was demonstrated in 1937 when Langley decided to build a successor to one of its most productive wind tunnels, the Variable Density Tunnel, or VDT.[14]

NACA officials felt that the expense of a VDT replacement could not be justified to congressional overseers; they simply would not understand the urgency. But the NACA Main Committee could obtain funding for a new tunnel if it was to be devoted to icing experiments. By 1937, many aircraft crashes traced to icing problems were attracting considerable public attention. Commercial airline operators were also clamoring for useful information on the subject. Thus Langley

began construction of an "ice" tunnel in May 1937.[15]

Former NACA Langley employee W. Kemble Johnson recalled in a 1967 interview his role in the project:

We built it from scratch—I mean, we were poor people. At Fort Eustis [a nearby Army base] we scrounged steel, trusses and columns that had been torn down and were laying in the weeds with trees practically growing through them. Because they were twisted and out of shape I had burners and welders come in…. [They] straightened out the trusses… took columns… cut the ends off and welded another column to them to get the height.… For less than $100,000 we built the whole building and wind tunnel and the works….[16]

The ice tunnel's insulation came courtesy of the U.S. Navy. Surplus Navy life preservers were obtained, and high school students cut the vests open to fluff out the insulation before it was applied. The refrigeration system consisted of dry ice, automobile carloads of which were unloaded by the same intrepid students. The first operational run of the tunnel came at night and presented a rather eerie sight. An opaque dry-ice fog hung above the floor and, Johnson reported, "The light would shine down on us and we'd walk around with just our heads sticking up. On top of [that fog] layer... was about a half-inch thick layer of mosquitoes with their jaws open." It was, he concluded, "a very weird thing."

The ice tunnel was used only for a brief series of experiments before conversion to a low-turbulence wind tunnel. Eventually, parts of the ice tunnel were used in the development of the test section and entrance cone of the

The Variable Density Tunnel arrives by rail in 1922 from the Newport News Shipbuilding and Dry Dock Company.

NASA Langley photo no. EL-2000-00529

The Lunar Landing Research Facility, now the Impact Dynamics Facility.

NASA Langley photo no. EL-2001-00424

Vacuum spheres of the Hypersonic Facilities Complex with a dusting of snow.

NASA Langley photo no. L-1969-02164

Low-Turbulence Pressure Tunnel.[17] In the battle of wits and pocketbooks, at least in this instance, the Laboratory had emerged the victor.

If there were ways to get around funding bottlenecks, there were also ways to get around research restrictions in the wind tunnels themselves. Langley wind tunnel studies were sometimes not officially approved; the practice of "bootlegging"—unauthorized, if imaginative, research—has occurred over the years. Two of the more ambitious Langley bootleggers were Arthur Kantrowitz and Eastman Jacobs. In 1938 the pair undertook what is believed to have been the world's first attempt to construct a nuclear fusion reactor. The project was abruptly canceled, however, when discovered one day by Dr. George Lewis, the NACA director of research, who was visiting from NACA headquarters in Washington.[18]

Tunnel work has also presented a degree of physical risk. High pressures can lead to explosions; structural failure of fan blades can tear a building apart. In one instance that occurred in the late 1950s, two technicians were blown right out of a tunnel into a nearby swamp when pressurized air was improperly vented. Fortunately, both survived. In another mishap around the same time, a test run of a high-temperature tunnel that used superheated pebbles resulted in a score of minor fires when the pebbles were inadvertently ejected outside of the tunnel. Paint was even burned off nearby cars.

Barton Geer, who retired in 1981 as Langley's director for Systems Engineering and Operations, was introduced to the perils of wind tunnel research in 1942. As a recently arrived junior engineer, he was sent to work in the 19-Foot Pressure Tunnel. One day, Geer was instructed to take pressure and humidity readings in the tunnel's test section. To do so he had to enter an airlock. But, says Geer, "In the early years, we did not think about safety like we do now. So the fellow who put me in there went home and forgot all about me. I didn't know how to work the airlock to get out. I was thinking, 'What's going on here? What's my wife going to think?' Fortunately, around midnight he said, 'My gosh— Bart's still in there!' So he came back and got me out."

In recognition of their contributions to aeronautical science, three Langley tunnels were declared National Historic Landmarks in 1985 by the U.S. Department of the Interior: the Variable Density, 30- by 60-Foot, and 8-Foot High-Speed Tunnels. Two other facilities—the Lunar Landing Research Facility and the Rendezvous Docking Simulator—were also proclaimed Historic Landmarks.

Take human ingenuity out of the picture and Langley wind tunnels are nothing more than expensive amalgamations of steel, bricks, mortar, and sophisticated equipment. Allow for human drive and creativity, as Langley has done, and these state-of-the-art "tools" can be seen for what they are: among the wisest capital investments the federal government has ever made.

BEYOND BRAINPOWER

No one factor can be isolated as the sole agent responsible for Langley's technological prominence in aeronautics. There does seem to have been something of a Langley cultural "formula"—a mix

The 1934 Aircraft Engineering Conference attendees in the Full-Scale Tunnel below a Boeing P-26A Peashooter. Orville Wright, Charles Lindbergh, and Howard Hughes were among the attendees.

NASA Langley photo no. EL-1996-00157

of sharp intellect, curiosity, humor, enthusiasm, competitiveness, personalities, and personality clashes—that enabled aeronautical researchers to do their best work. "What impressed me most about Langley," says Donald Hearth, director from 1975 to 1984, "and what made Langley so different, were the people. They were extremely creative, highly loyal, very competent, always worked well together, particularly when the challenge was great, and believed that they could do almost anything." Exceptionally able hands also appear to have held the management reins. Many veterans credit men like George W. Lewis, the first NACA director of research, and Langley engineers in charge with setting the Center on the proper course and guiding it through the shoals of project selection and program expansion. (By 1960, with the appoint-

ment of Floyd Thompson, the title of the individual overseeing Langley was changed to Center Director.)

Regardless of how it exercised its expertise, Langley had enough to spare. Langley exported its organizational and engineering talent, first to Langley's daughter NACA laboratories and, later, to NASA Headquarters in Washington, D.C., and to the emerging space Centers. In the opinions of some, it is not overstating matters to describe Langley organizational know-how as crucial to the success of the U.S. crewed space program. "One of our primary 'products' has been people: leaders, really, in the aerospace field," Paul Holloway maintains. "We sent groups to found other Centers, like Dryden, Lewis (now Glenn), Ames, and Wallops. Many went on to Washington and played major roles in agency management. In 1961 and 1962, a group left

NASA Langley photo no. L-1995-06377

Langley employees attend the closing ceremony for the Full-Scale Tunnel, which is now operated by Old Dominion University.

here to start Johnson Space Center—totally from scratch."

Langley engineers might have been bright and creative, and the leaders adept at technology management, but the Laboratory was not immune to the petty suspicions that inevitably arise when a small town becomes the home of those thought to be outsiders. In the early years of Langley's existence there was something of a culture clash between the local populace and the professional Laboratory staff. A significant percentage of that staff came from more populous areas in the North and Midwest, where amusements were many and easy to come by. Hampton was southern, rural, isolated, a place to make fun of but not a place in which to have fun. Hamptonians were made uneasy by the brash confidence displayed by the NACA

"Yankees." Matters were not improved when, in response to their cool reception, some Langley researchers did not hesitate to tell the locals on what side of the streetcar they should get off.

"Hampton was a sleepy fishing town. As the saying goes, you could fire a cannon down Main Street at 9:00 p.m. and not hit anyone," remembers Don Baals, who came to work at Langley in 1939 and who retired in 1975 as assistant chief of the Full-Scale Research Division. "The Hampton people viewed these [NACA] people with a degree of trepidation. But the problem was solved when the young men married into the local families."

For years the phrase "Nacka nut" (Nacka is the verbalization of NACA) was heard around Hampton and surrounding environs. The detail-oriented

Barrel-joust competition at Langley picnic at Buckroe Beach.

NASA Langley photo no. EL-2000-00351

Langley engineer, it was said, would venture into hardware stores and ask that lumber be cut to the nearest sixteenth of an inch, which was considered to be a ridiculously precise amount. Or a hapless appliance salesman would be waylaid and asked to detail the manufacturer's specifications for a vacuum cleaner, including the number of revolutions per minute made by the electric motor.[19]

Once, or so the story goes, a Laboratory engineer bought a hand-cranked ice-cream maker from a local hardware store. The appliance came with a rust-proof guarantee. Three weeks after the purchase, the engineer returned; the maker was a rusted ruin. The store owner replaced the original with another, also guaranteed against rust. Another three weeks went by and the engineer returned, with the second maker in the same condition as the first. Again a free replacement was provided. Two weeks later, the engineer was back, this time with a third rust-encrusted ice-cream maker. Incredulous, the hardware store owner asked the engineer exactly how he made his ice cream. The engineer replied that he would make no ice cream until he was satisfied that the maker was really rustproof. Therefore, the engineer added, he had filled the makers up with salt water and let them sit in his back yard. Thus far, none had passed the test.

The owner promptly refunded the engineer's money and told him never again to think about buying an ice-cream maker—or anything else, for that matter—from that particular hardware store.

As time passed, negative encounters between Langley employees and Hampton residents became far less

NASA Langley photo no. EL-2000-00346

The NACA cowling on a Curtiss AT-5A at Langley in 1928.

NASA Langley photo no. EL-2001-00444

In 1959, then-Langley researcher Francis Rogallo examines the Rogallo Wing in the 7- by 10-Foot Tunnel. Designed to bring spacecraft to a controlled soft landing, the concept was embraced by hang-gliding enthusiasts.

frequent. The locals grew accustomed to the accents and habits of the young researchers who came to Hampton from all over the country. Many rented rooms in area boardinghouses, ingratiating themselves slowly but surely into the community's daily routines.

Apart from their standing in Hampton at large, those working at Langley Laboratory enjoyed themselves among themselves. Laboratory staff developed a lively social circuit: a club for model-airplane enthusiasts; touch football, basketball, and softball teams; rounds of parties; regular outings to nearby beaches; frequent dances; and periodic gatherings of every sort. Some were talented musicians and delighted

Richard Whitcomb with model designed with area rule in 8-Foot High Speed Tunnel in 1955.

NASA Langley photo no. EL-2000-00401

An Apollo model in the slotted-throat 16-Foot Transonic Tunnel in 1964.

NASA Langley photo no. EL-2001-00370

The High-Speed Frontier, Becker recalls that, even during World War II, sometimes a good diversion was nothing more than a well-thought-out practical joke:

The staff relaxed through all of the usual sports and social events with little apparent effect of wartime pressures. Five of us had formed an informal golfing group.... [My boss John] Stack had never played before and had no clubs of his own, but we offered to lend him an old bag with a broken strap and some of our spare clubs.... [Henry] Fedziuk, who was the chief humorist of the group, had often been the butt of Stack's practical jokes and saw here a welcome chance to turn the tables.

With enthusiastic help from some of the rest of us he lined the bottom of Stack's bag with some 10 pounds of sheet lead. We also made sure the bag had a full complement of clubs, and we told Stack that caddies were used only by the rich and decrepit. By the start of the back nine, with a score card showing well over a hundred in spite of considerable cheating, Stack was seen to start dragging the bag along behind him....

His expletives [became] louder and more colorful, and a short time later he discovered what had been done. Understandably, he always examined his equipment very suspiciously at subsequent sessions.[20]

their colleagues with prowess on the piano or other musical instruments. Others were singers and one or two were able amateur magicians.

While the Langley staff was serious about work, they were serious about fun, too. John Becker began his work at Langley Laboratory in 1936 and retired in 1975 as chief of the High-Speed Aerodynamics Division. In his book

The spirit of camaraderie extended to the labs, where cooperation and collaboration were seen as a virtue. But there was also a good-humored rivalry. "There was enormous technical competition between the divisions at Langley," recalls Israel Taback, who arrived at Langley in the early 1940s and who, upon retirement from Langley in 1976, was the chief engineer on Viking, the first project to ever soft-land a robot probe on Mars. "People would fight with each other over technical details. That was all very healthy. The end result was a battle of ideas—ideas that had merit tended to float to the surface. The good ideas won."

That Langley was an environment suited to achievement was underscored by the multitude of national and international awards won by staff members over the years. Perhaps none was more prized than the Collier Trophy, named in honor of publisher, sportsman, and aviator Robert J. Collier. Since 1910 the Collier has been awarded annually for the greatest achievements in American aeronautics (and recently for astronautics achievements as well). Langley researchers have been thus acknowledged five times: in 1929, for a low-drag engine cowling; in 1946, for research on airplane icing; in 1947, for supersonic flight research; in 1951, for development of the slotted-throat transonic wind tunnel; and in 1954, for the transonic area rule.

The point can be made that, since relatively little was known about the specifics of flight, it was inevitable that Langley researchers would unearth something that could be productively applied to the flying of aircraft. But nothing is ever guaranteed. That Langley Laboratory achieved what it did is tribute to the talent and drive of the staff and the savvy of NACA officials and supervisors who knew when and how to exercise control. Langley's ultimate contribution was not that of the manufacturer, for the Laboratory would never build airplanes. Rather, Langley donated its intellectual currency to the advancement of aircraft; its true value to the aeronautical industry and the Nation was that of aeronautical trailblazer as testified by its technical documents.

In time, later generations of flying machines would surpass the Wright *Flyer* in the same way that a modern automobile outstrips a primitive two-wheel cart. Prowess in the atmosphere led directly to success in space. Ever more sophisticated craft would be developed. Yet close to seven decades would pass before humankind was able to make the long leap from the Wrights on the wind-swept Carolina beach to the Sea of Tranquility on the Moon. During that time, Langley Research Center would contribute to ventures that would have appeared preposterous to even the most visionary of 19th century aeronautical pioneers.

Close to seven decades would pass before humankind was able to make the long leap from a wind-swept Carolina beach to the Moon's Sea of Tranquillity.

NASA Langley photo no. EL-2001-00480

The circular test section and control room of NACA Tunnel No. 1 with a model of a Curtiss Jenny.

CHAPTER

3

REFINING THE AIRPLANE

High above the mud, blood, and gas attacks of World War I trench warfare flew remarkably flimsy craft that were, by the standards of the day, a stunning technological advance. Here was proof that the airplane was an invention with which to reckon. The plane was no longer a comic extravagance nor an adult toy; the outbreak of military conflict mandated a darker purpose—that of a powerful agent of war. As the aircraft of the warring powers sparred with one another in the world's first dogfights, it was quite clear that the airplane's role had been forever altered.

At war's end, with the European rail system in shambles, the role of the airplane was again expanded, this time as an instrument of commerce. The private sector aviation industry slowly began to grow, led by individuals determined to find a profitable niche in the transportation of people and goods. There were certainly plenty of equipment and skilled workers, for war had provided an abundance of aircraft and pilots willing to fly them.

Within three months after the November 1918 armistice, commercial aviation began in Germany as Deutsche Luftreederei inaugurated passenger-carrying service. That same year, daily flights between London and Paris commenced. The first passenger flights between U.S. cities followed in 1920, and by 1925 regular airfreight service between Chicago and Detroit had been established.[1]

NACA test pilot in fur-lined leather flight suit with oxygen face mask before a Vought VE-7 in 1927.

NASA Langley photo no. EL-1999-00284

A test pilot and an engineer prepare for a research flight in 1920.

NASA Langley photo no. EL-2000-00319

U.S. Navy dirigible *U.S.S. Los Angeles* during turning radius tests in 1928.

NASA Langley photo no. EL-1999-00286

Everyone, it seemed, either wanted to fly in an "aeroplane" or knew someone that did. Enthusiasts predicted that the airplane's exciting childhood would usher in a brighter, faster future. Soon, speculated these starry-eyed proponents, there would be a personal airplane in every garage. It was simply a matter of time. The general public was becoming accustomed to the drone of aircraft engines overhead, to the sight of goggle- and leather-clad aviators, and to the notion of sending or receiving airmail. However, in physical and economic terms flight remained a relatively risky business. Crashes were not uncommon. With the exception of a handful of hardy commercial carriers that pampered well-to-do clients and ferried mail under contract, few American companies found profit in aviation. The federal government and the military remained the primary buyers of new aircraft and the sponsors of most aeronautical research.[2] Fortunately for the commercial aviation industry, the nonstop transatlantic flight of aviation pioneer Charles Lindbergh in 1927—coming as it did almost a quarter century after the Wright *Flyer* rose above the sands of Kitty Hawk—dramatically changed the situation.

Wedged into what essentially was a flying gas tank with wings, Lindbergh dared the wide Atlantic and won. His touchdown at an airfield outside Paris on a cool May night set off wild celebrations on two continents. But Lindbergh's gutsy accomplishment was more than a personal triumph, for it proved that the airplane could conquer great distances. Lucky Lindy's success drew worldwide attention to the airplane's ocean-crossing potential and, not incidentally, inspired an entire generation of young,

Fred Weick, left in cockpit, and Charles Lindbergh, right in cockpit, with Tom Hamilton at Langley in 1927.

NASA Langley photo no. EL-2000-00522

aeronautical engineers and aviators. By the late 1930s, coast-to-coast air service was a routine fact of life and "flying boats" were beginning regular treks of transpacific routes.[3]

Just after World War I, the bulk of Langley research was still aimed squarely at solutions to problems of specific concern to the military. But by the late 1920s, as the importance of commercial aviation increased, so did the time the Laboratory devoted to study of aeronautical items of interest to the private sector. Fortunately, what had been learned in Langley studies of military aircraft design could usually be applied, with minor modification, to civil aviation. (By the late 1930s, military and private sector interests were diverging, as the military became interested in higher speeds and altitudes while commercial carriers emphasized safety and efficient operation.)[4]

By 1927, aeronautical research at the NACA Langley Laboratory was in full swing. Extensive theoretical and

experimental work was being done on lighter-than-air (LTA) craft—known popularly as airships or dirigibles—in tandem with the U.S. Army. Langley personnel conducted tests to determine takeoff, landing, and docking procedures and assisted in speed and deceleration measurements. As a result, writes *Engineer In Charge* author James Hansen, many Langley flight researchers became outspoken advocates of airships.

It was not clear at the time that the airplane would win out over the airship. Airplanes of the early 1920s were slow and small—an aerodynamicist who favored airships over airplanes even went to the bother of proving that airplanes larger than those of the day could never be built. LTA advocates believed correctly that airships had enormous unproven capabilities. They were not much slower and could carry many more passengers in far greater comfort than airplanes, most of which still had open cockpits. They were much more forgiving than airplanes during instrument flight. With their extreme range and low operating cost, they could be used not just as military weapons but also for transportation of heavy commercial and industrial loads.

Unfortunately, the accident on May 6, 1937, that destroyed the dirigible Hindenburg as it attempted to dock in Lakehurst, New Jersey—23 crew and 13 passengers lost their lives when the airship burst into flames—also resulted in the economic collapse of the 20-year-old LTA passenger-carrying industry.[5]

Simultaneous with its LTA studies, Langley continued aircraft research. New models manufactured by such companies as Curtiss, Martin, Sperry, Vought, Douglas, and Boeing underwent evaluation at the Laboratory. The work at Langley contributed to an improving airplane: one that was becoming safer, faster, stronger, and easier to handle. But the plane was far from perfect. Designing the best possible aircraft proved to be a trade-off between desirable characteristics, such as speed and range. Moreover, the forces that permit and constrain flight are complex. Understanding them required time, determination, and ingenuity.

ON THE JOB

The first building erected at Langley was, by modern standards, a modest affair. Built by the New York City firm J. G. White Engineering Corporation at a cost of $80,900 in 1917-era dollars, the structure contained administrative and drafting offices, machine and woodworking shops, and photographic and instrumentation labs. The first wind tunnel at the Laboratory was housed separately in a small brick and concrete building. By 1922 the Langley complex had grown to include two wind tunnel facilities, two engine dynamometer laboratories, and a large airplane hangar. Research was being conducted on better flight instrumentation and ways to reduce aerodynamic drag, increase lift, boost propulsion efficiency, and improve structural integrity.[6]

For more than a dozen years after its official formation, the Langley professional staff numbered less than 100, a figure that was not surpassed until 1930. (By 1927 support staff had grown to 104 individuals.) That this relatively small complement would repeatedly produce top-notch results might have been due to the balance between structure and independence, a dynamic that author James Hansen terms "careful bureaucratic restraint [and] research freedom." At Langley there was great institutional reluctance to announce results of studies until researchers and their superiors were confident that those results would bear up even under the toughest scrutiny. Researchers were therefore free to work creatively on novel ideas without the fear of preliminary reports building up too much industry anticipation of and pressure for future advances.[7]

The Langley working atmosphere was one of informality. Everyone knew everyone else, and the most junior could become acquainted with the engineer in charge. There was an organizational chart, but it was seen more as a necessary evil. "Titles were tall cotton. People were not here for self-glorification," says William D. Mace, who came to Langley in 1948 and who retired in 1989 as director for Electronics. "The thing that held folks together out here was their common interest: the ability to do first-class

Langley in May 1930 with the Full-Scale Tunnel under construction in the foreground.

NASA Langley photo no. EL-2001-00473

Full-Scale Tunnel under construction in 1930.

NASA Langley photo no. EL-1999-00355

NACA Langley Laboratory and U.S. Army Langley Field in 1933. Buildings with checkerboard roofs are U.S. Army airplane hangers.

NASA Langley photo no. EL-2001-00392

A Langley carpenter
prepares airplane wings for
research flights in 1920.

NASA Langley photo no. EL-2001-00373

Patternmakers manufacture
and assemble a wing
skeleton for inflight
pressure distribution tests
in 1922.

NASA Langley photo no. EL-1999-00257

A Ford model A with a
"Huck starter" cranking an
airplane engine in 1924.

NASA Langley photo no. EL-1997-00132

aeronautics research. The fact is, Langley produced. If it had not, it would have disappeared."

In the first decades of its existence Langley management did its best to keep a safe distance between the Laboratory and bureaucrats in the Nation's capital. John Becker, writing in *The High-Speed Frontier*, observes that the Langley of the 1930s did not think of itself as part of the federal bureaucracy. Langley was "spiritually and physically separated from Washington. The staff had been largely handpicked in one way or another to form an elite group unique in the federal system... [There was] a beneficial sense of family."

As in any family, at Langley there were occasional disputes, personality clashes, and struggles over the nature and extent of research programs. Whatever problems arose were refereed by management, a group small in number but fiercely dedicated to Langley's flight-research mission. Managers did not mind dirtying their hands; indeed, many relished it. That Laboratory management was of the hands-on variety soon became evident even to the most junior engineer. John Becker writes of his introduction to the Langley management style while preparing an experiment in the 8-Foot Tunnel:

One night during my second week on the job, just before I closed the airlock doors at the entrance to the test chamber for a test run, an unusual-looking stranger dressed in hunting clothes came in and stood there watching my preparations. [My supervisor] had advised me not to allow visitors in the test chamber during a high-speed run primarily because the pressure dropped quickly to

about two-thirds of an atmosphere, the equivalent of a 12,000 foot altitude.

Assuming that the visitor had come in from one of the numerous duck blinds along Back River, I said firmly, "I will have to ask you to leave now." Making no move he said, "I am Reid," in such ponderous and authoritative tones that I quickly realized it was Langley's Engineer In Charge whom I had not yet met.

No one had told me that Reid, who lived only a couple of miles from Langley Field, often came out in the evening, especially when tests of electrical equipment were being made (he was an electrical engineer)....[8]

Today there is much talk about how to improve the efficiency of public and private enterprise. The intent is to eliminate unnecessary layers of management in awkward command-and-control systems, systems that centralize power, reward bureaucracy, and stifle creativity. From the very beginning Langley had few such problems. Laboratory management encouraged the free flow of ideas, whether they came from a grizzled veteran or a recently hired junior engineer. If an idea had merit, a junior engineer could approach his superiors without fear of reproach. If the idea was successfully adopted, the individual proposing it would receive full and proper credit.

There was a brisk exchange of ideas at Langley in discussions not only limited to the lab. Some of Langley's best work was done while researchers were out to lunch—literally. Most of the professional staff assembled on a daily basis in the second-floor lunchroom of the Laboratory administration building. Plate lunches could be bought there for 25 or 30 cents (35 cents on days steak was

Langley lunch room with marble top tables that researchers used as sketch pads during discussions.

NASA Langley photo no. EL-2001-00440

served). The lunch tables had white marble tops, a feature that was a great boon to technical discussions. Researchers could and did draw curves, sketches, and equations directly on the table during animated exchanges. Such marks could easily be erased with a hand or napkin. "It was exciting and inspiring for a young new arrival to sit down in the crowded lunchroom and find himself surrounded by the well-known engineers who had authored the NACA papers he had been studying as a student," John Becker writes in *The High-Speed Frontier*. "There were no formal personnel development or training programs in those days, but I realize now that these daily lunchroom contacts provided not only an intimate view of a fascinating variety of live career models, but also an unsurpassed source of stimulation, advice, ideas, and amusement."

However challenging and intellectually exciting Langley's aeronautical research was, it was far from glamorous. Young engineers worked long, hard hours. The recently hired paid their dues by laboriously plotting by hand the data collected from wind tunnels, supervising the mounting of models, turning valves, watching gauges, and generally making sure that everything was shipshape

before wind tunnel tests were run. The work was routine, even boring, but for engineers in love with aeronautics, the rigors of the work paled in comparison to what could be, and was, learned.

There was a certain price to pay for the Langley can-do reputation. As the Laboratory attracted more national attention, it began to lose some of its best and brightest to the booming private sector, which beckoned with higher salaries and hard-to-refuse research opportunities. Between 1920 and 1937, thirty-seven professional staff left Langley for aeronautical careers elsewhere.[9] Considering Langley's size, such a loss was significant. As James Hansen notes, though the personnel losses may have delayed the successful execution of a few NACA research projects, the larger American aeronautics effort probably benefitted from the loss. Langley provided a training ground for dozens of aeronautical experts and an apprenticeship that was excellent preparation for a university career or a job with a major aircraft manufacturer.[10]

Many who came to work at Langley intended to stay but a few years and then move on. However, not all who thought of the Laboratory as a professional stepping-stone followed through on their original intentions. Langley's character, its sense of community, its technical culture, its strong sense of self and mission, the sheer number of aerodynamics challenges that confronted its staff, and the chance to make a difference: these were persuasive arguments that convinced not a few to stay at the Laboratory. Certainly, for those who elected to remain, there would be no shortage of interesting projects.

NACA hanger as it appeared around 1933.

NASA Langley photo no. EL-2001-00378

A W-1 with tricycle landing gear designed by Fred Wieck in the Full-Scale Tunnel in 1934.

NASA Langley photo no. EL-2000-00355

BREAKING THROUGH

Exactly how it is that human beings make an intuitive leap from half thought out idea to sound concept remains something of a mystery. What is not mysterious is that chances for making the right connections increase the longer one works at it. Perhaps Thomas Edison said it best when he described genius as consisting of 1 percent inspiration and 99 percent perspiration. Hard work was the norm at Langley, but it was work that the researchers eagerly embraced. Moti-

vating them was a feeling similar to that felt by pioneers crossing unexplored territory: anticipation, enthusiasm, and a sense of pending accomplishment. "Langley engineers knew they were making fundamental contributions toward understanding how an airplane flew," says John C. Houbolt, who came to Langley in 1942 and who retired in 1985 as the Center's chief aeronautical scientist (13 of those years were spent in the private sector). "Langley was breaking through, on the frontiers of technology."

In the 1920s, Langley's young engineers whittled steadily away at a block of assorted aeronautical problems. One of the most difficult dilemmas was that of speed: how to make planes fly faster while maintaining acceptable safety standards and operating efficiencies. Langley's high-speed research, begun in the 1920s, continued even as speeds geometrically increased. Laboratory researchers also worked on small-scale projects with precise objectives, like the instrument program to measure such things as engine torque, revolutions per minute, propeller thrust, airspeed, and angle of attack (the angle at which aircraft wings meet the onrushing flow of air). In addition, there were projects to gauge stresses on airplanes while in flight and upon landing and attempts to develop better, more responsive controls.[11]

A landmark event in Langley's early history was the installation, in 1922, of the Variable Density Tunnel, or VDT. It had inherent limitations: among them, small model size and low speed of airflow. As the first two words in the name suggests, the VDT allowed for air to be pressurized up to 20 atmospheres (1 atmosphere being the normal pressure of air at sea level). At the higher pressures, or atmospheres, accurate aerodynamic information could be obtained by monitoring the flow of air over small models.[12]

The VDT was not pretty—it resembled a giant, corrugated, hollow lozenge—but its appearance belied handsome research results. Studies conducted in the VDT, beginning in 1923, culminated in the 1933 release of an NACA report that detailed 78 different airfoil, or wing shapes for aircraft, each designated by a four-digit number. Using the four-digit airfoil series from this report, several generations of aircraft designers were able to produce some of the finest

Eastman Jacobs, Shorty Defoe, Malvern Powell, and Harold Turner conduct tests with the Variable Density Tunnel in 1929.

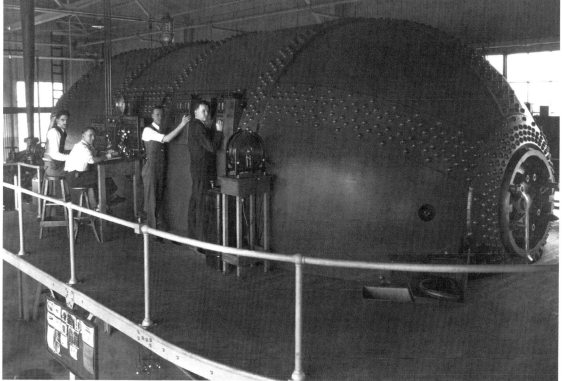

NASA Langley photo no. EL-1996-00143

military and civilian aircraft ever flown.[13] "Above all," write Don Baals and William R. Corliss in *Wind Tunnels of NASA*, "[the VDT] established NACA as a technically competent research organization. It was a technological quantum leap that rejuvenated American aerodynamic research and, in time, led to some of the best aircraft in the world."

Nor was the VDT a perfect instrument of research. It was repeatedly plagued by operational difficulties. When partially destroyed by an August 1927 fire, normal operations did not resume until December of 1930. Nevertheless, it was the first of a generation of Langley wind tunnels that would be acclaimed for its leading-edge capabilities.

Other research facilities at Langley grew out of specific requests. Early in 1928, the Assistant Secretary of Commerce for Aeronautics called a conference of military and government agencies, including the NACA, to study the

causes and prevention of ice formation on aircraft. Earlier, the Navy's Bureau of Aeronautics had made much the same request. The result was the NACA's first refrigerated wind tunnel, which began operations later that same year (and was quickly modified, as noted in Chapter 1) and was intended to study ice formation and prevention on wings and propellers of aircraft. These studies grew into a major effort that later won a Collier Trophy for NACA scientist Lewis A. Rodert, who conducted most of his basic research on thermal deicing from 1936 through 1940 while working in the Langley Flight Research Division.[14]

However productive were these in-house efforts, NACA officials were well aware that they needed to keep abreast of trends and developments in the larger aeronautics community. Accordingly, in May of 1926, the NACA inaugurated the first Aircraft Engineering Conference at Langley. These "inspections," as they

Wing model in the Variable Density Tunnel.

NASA Langley photo no. EL-1999-00285

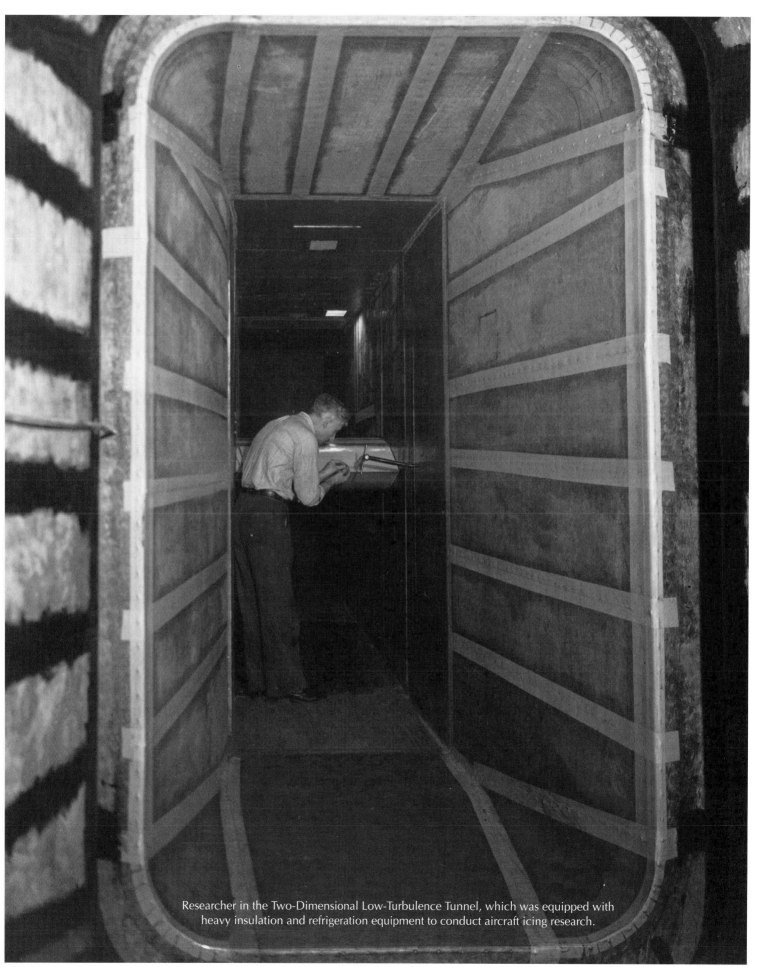

Researcher in the Two-Dimensional Low-Turbulence Tunnel, which was equipped with heavy insulation and refrigeration equipment to conduct aircraft icing research.

became known to Langley insiders, evolved into elaborate but useful annual events at which attendees assessed the Laboratory's progress and suggested areas of research that Langley might wish to pursue.[15]

The event grew from a modest and relaxed affair in 1926, when the NACA Main Committee sent out only 38 invitations, into a highly staged pageant that took weeks of preparation by the Langley and Washington office staffs. By 1936 the meeting took two days. Over 300 people attended each session, including a number of aviation writers who reported fully on the presentations in newspapers and journals. Discontinued during World War II, the conferences resumed in 1946 under a slightly different format and were eventually stretched to five days. In succeeding years, the inspections became semiannual affairs and rotated among various NACA facilities.[16]

One of Langley's most celebrated aeronautical contributions came about partly as a result of the second conference in 1927, during which private-sector representatives repeated a suggestion that had been made by the U.S. Navy's Bureau of Aeronautics a year earlier. Could a covering, or cowling, be designed to fit around the finned cylinders of radial aircraft engines then in widespread use? Both the Navy and industry were eager to reduce the high amount of drag associated with the cylinders, which, because they were arrayed like spokes in a wheel, jutted directly into the air stream during flight.[17]

Langley's subsequent low-drag cowling design was proof that the methodical approach to tough aeronautical problems

An interior view of the seaplane towing channel, where a variety of hull and pontoon shapes were evaluated.

NASA Langley photo no. EL-2001-00441

A plane fuselage mounted in the Propeller Research Tunnel in 1922.

NASA Langley photo no. EL-1999-00391

Curtiss Bleeker helicopter in front of the Langley hanger in 1930.

NASA Langley photo no. EL-2000-00352

A Langley test pilot, dressed for high altitude flight, in front of a Wright Apache without an engine cowling in 1928.

NASA Langley photo no. EL-2000-00341

Army Curtiss AT-5A with NACA cowling in 1928.

NASA Langley photo no. EL-1999-00305

paid dividends. First, a team headed by aviation pioneer and then Langley engineer Fred E. Weick designed ten different experimental cowlings and put them to the test in the recently built Propeller Research Tunnel (PRT), which could accommodate full-size operating engines and propellers. Elements of the design were systematically varied to determine how best to cool the engine while maintaining a streamlined shape. Results were carefully collected and examined. Once the optimum cowl shape had been identified, air vanes and baffles were redesigned to direct the airflow to cool the hottest portions of the cylinders and crankcase. The final product, entitled simply "NACA cowling no. 10," caused an immediate sensation when its performance was made public. The cowling not only reduced drag, but also substantially improved engine cooling.[18]

Flight tests of the cowling indicated that, from drag reduction alone, flight speeds could be increased by 16 percent. A technical paper authored by Weick that explained the specifics was released in November 1928. The NACA announced to the press that if the cowling (estimated cost: $25) was installed on existing aircraft, then the possible annual savings in fuel and associated costs could amount to over $5 million—more, said politically astute officials, than the total of all NACA appropriations through 1928.[19]

Confirmation of cowling no. 10's drag-reducing abilities was provided by Frank Hawks, a stunt flyer and barnstorming pilot. Flying an NACA-cowl-equipped Lockheed Air Express from Los Angeles to New York nonstop in February 1929, Hawks increased his craft's maximum speed from 157 to 177 mph and set a new coast-to-coast record of 18 hours, 13 minutes. A day following the feat, the NACA received the following telegram:

Cooling carefully checked and O.K. Record impossible without new cowling. All credit due NACA for painstaking and accurate research. [Signed] Gerry Vultee, Lockheed Aircraft Co.[20]

Several months later, the NACA won its first Collier Trophy. The airplane design revolution had begun.

The NACA cowling became the standard enclosure for air-cooled radial engines and in succeeding years was continually revised and improved. The reduction in drag afforded by the new cowling led designers to ask for, and the NACA to look for, other areas where drag could be substantially reduced. Looking back, it was clear that in the cowling design Langley researchers had

Curtiss Jenny airplane trails a pitot-static tube for air pressure measurements.

NASA Langley photo no. EL-2001-00375

Open-circuit air intake for first wind tunnel.

NASA Langley photo no. EL-2000-00526

Fabricating airplane engine cowlings in the metal shop.

NASA Langley photo no. EL-2000-00348

fully applied the aerodynamics lessons they were learning. Writes James Hansen in *Engineer In Charge*: "The cowling was the product of fruitful engineering science: a solid combination of physical understanding, intuition, systematic experimentation and applied mathematics." More than any other project in its first full decade of existence, the Langley cowling design effort cemented the NACA's reputation as an organization that knew airplanes and how to better them.

THE SHAPE OF THINGS TO COME

As work progressed at Langley in the early 1930s, a new sort of airplane was emerging from the drafting boards of aircraft industry designers. The wood and fabric that made up the original biplanes were gradually being replaced by metal. By decade's end, most new airplanes were built entirely of metal. The biplane's externally braced double wing gave way to a single, internally braced wing. Landing gear became retractable and the engine was lighter, more powerful, and covered by a cowling. The propeller had variable pitch, which meant that propeller angles of attack could be adjusted according to flight speed, permitting aircraft engines, for the first time, to operate at maximum efficiency either at low or high speeds.[21]

For all the progress being made in airplane flightworthiness, designers still had an incomplete understanding of the interaction between the aerodynamic forces acting on an aircraft and the aircraft's structural response to those forces. Two areas of particular concern to researchers were aeroelastic divergence—the tendency of aircraft to twist and bend while in flight—and flutter—destructive vibrations of a structure reacting to an unsteady airflow. Flutter is thought to have been partially responsible for the 1931 in-flight breakup of a Fokker trimotor, which caused the deaths of famed Notre Dame football coach Knute Rockne and six others. Theoretical analyses by Theodore Thoedorsen and Isadore Garrick developed at Langley provided a means to calculate the unsteady aerodynamic forces causing flutter, thereby allowing engineers to suggest ways to structurally modify or strengthen the most flutter-susceptible parts of aircraft.[22]

In 1940 Langley formally dedicated the Structures Laboratory, its first facility devoted strictly to the study of aircraft structures. There, researchers worked on ways of making an airplane's metal skin stiffer and stronger and examined methods to internally brace the weakest areas. Fatigue—the tendency of metal structures to buckle or break after repeated use—was also investigated. Fatigue experiments done at Langley and elsewhere eventually led to "rip-stop" designs that minimized crack propagation (the tendency of a small tear to become a catastrophic rip) by reinforcing an airplane's frame at key points.[23]

If there was one airplane that epitomized the design revolution of the 1930s, it was the Douglas DC-3 transport. Langley had an active role in developing or evaluating the DC-3's aeronautical innovations, which included internally braced wings, wing flaps, retractable landing gear, cowled engines, controllable pitch propellers, a geared

NASA Langley photo no. EL-2000-00350

Airplane engine cowlings being installed on a test airplane.

NASA Langley photo no. EL-2001-00454

Langley operations crew in front of Fokker trimotor with newly installed NACA cowlings.

NASA Langley photo no. EL-2002-00166

Structures Research Laboratory just after completion in 1940.

Full-Scale Tunnel (left) and seaplane towing facility (right) in 1930.

NASA Langley photo no. EL-2001-00476

The 19-Foot Pressure Tunnel in 1939.

NASA Langley photo no. EL-2001-00159

Douglas YO-31A airplane in the Full-Scale Tunnel.

NASA Langley photo no. EL-2001-00377

supercharger, and an all-metal, stressed-skin construction.[24]

The DC-3, which first flew in December 1935 and was in airline operation by the summer of 1936, was large enough to carry 21 passengers. With this number of passengers and a cruising speed of 185 mph at 10,000 feet, airlines had for the first time an aircraft with operating costs sufficiently low so that a profit could be made without complete dependence on revenue from airmail contracts. The craft was, as pilots described it, "one tough bird": although easy to handle, the DC-3 could absorb structural punishment and keep on flying. By 1940, the existing fleet of DC-3s had flown 100 million miles, carried nearly 3 million passengers and had become the dominant airplane of its time.[25]

Langley's contributions to the development of an aircraft such as the DC-3 would not have been possible without additional state-of-the-art research facilities, which, by the early 1930s, were becoming operational at the Laboratory. In 1931, for instance, the Full-Scale Tunnel joined Langley's wind tunnel roster. Into its 30- by 60-foot test section a modest two-story house could comfortably fit; most aircraft of the era could easily be accommodated as well. (The Full-Scale Tunnel exists still, refurbished and renamed the 30- by 60-Foot Tunnel, and is now operated by Old Dominion University under the terms of an agreement with NASA.) By mid-1931 a hydrodynamics facility—known at Langley as the Towing Tank—was also put into operation. Originally 2,000 feet long, it was later extended to 2,900 feet and was used primarily to determine the performance characteristics of various hull designs for seaplanes and amphibious

vehicles. By towing model hulls through the water from a standing start to simulate takeoff speed, researchers could suggest changes in or improvements to basic designs.[26]

By 1935, the 15-Foot Spin Tunnel had been built and by the late 1930s a series of high-speed tunnels—the 11-Inch, 24-Inch, and 8-Foot—were completed. The 24-Inch High-Speed Tunnel was especially productive: by 1939, tests of airfoils therein had led to the design of the propellers that powered the American fighters to over 400 mph, thus enabling the fighters to rule the European and Asian skies in the last years of World War II.[27]

In 1936, the 8-Foot High-Speed Tunnel began operations. There new aircraft models could, for the first time, be evaluated at speeds in excess of 500 mph. Based on pioneering investigations conducted in this facility, researchers were able to delineate the specific stability and control problems encountered in high-speed dives. Practical aircraft products that resulted from the studies included a dive recovery flap, high-speed low-drag engine cowlings, a new family of air inlets for jet-propelled aircraft, and designs for propellers that powered aircraft to over 500 mph.[28]

Early in 1937, a contract was awarded to begin construction of the 19-Foot Pressure Tunnel, which became operational two years later. There, under 2.5 atmospheres of pressure, various aircraft control and flap systems were examined, as well as designs for a number of World War II era airplanes. When more advanced tunnels were developed later, the 19-Foot was assigned to research in aircraft aeroelasticity and high-speed flutter.[29] Eventually the

Instrument panel of a
Fairchilld FC-2W2 in 1928.

NASA Langley photo no. EL-2001-00366

facility found new life, with Dupont Freon™ gas as a test medium, a new 16-foot test section, and a new name: the Transonic Dynamics Tunnel.

By the late 1930s, Fred Weick, of NACA cowling fame, had devised an effective, if unconventional, tricycle landing gear, improving upon a design introduced by the Wright brothers. Weick positioned a single strut with a tire under the plane's nose and a wheel under each wing. Because the two main wheels were behind the plane's center of gravity and the nose wheel was steerable, it was far easier to taxi and land an airplane. Pilots favored the improvement in visibility—the plane sat more level on the runway—and passengers were grateful that they no longer had to scramble up and down inclined aisles. Prototype versions appeared in the late 1930s and by the late

1940s nearly all U.S. commercial and military aircraft employed the tricycle concept or a version thereof.[30]

By Langley's 22nd anniversary in 1939, the world had been made a different place by the advent of ocean-crossing airplanes. Travelers were crossing the Atlantic and Pacific Oceans in increasing numbers. By contemporary standards, air travel was slow and time consuming—a trip from London to New York on Pan American Airways' "flying hotel," the B-314, took 23 hours—but stylish and comfortable nonetheless. The introduction of Pan Am's China Clippers and the construction of island-based resorts and refueling depots made passenger-carrying transpacific flight feasible, even enjoyable. The airplane had become an intercontinental, paying proposition.[31]

Synthetic vision cockpit
display during flight test
in 1999.

NASA Langley photo no. EL-1999-00671

"Many people knowing aviation considered that [commercial] transoceanic flight would forever be impossible," remarked famed aeronautical-design pioneer Igor Sikorsky in an interview conducted in October 1971. "[But] the NACA by [its] work... certainly helped to produce these ships and certainly helped to bring and keep America in the first place in commercial aviation. Military too, but commercial aviation was definitely first because of the very excellent scientific work which this organization produced."[32]

The airplane had ascended to youthful prominence directly after World War I as a carrier of people and goods. Its vigorous adolescence in the 1930s was marked by substantial design changes and the further maturation of globe-girding commercial markets. But political conflict would again drive technological change. By 1940 the planet was embroiled in yet another worldwide conflict, a struggle that would prove more terrible and destructive than the first. World War II would provide the impetus for the airplane's next evolutionary leap.

Model Bell X-5, tested at Langley, shows two extreme positions of variable wing sweep.

CHAPTER

4

SWORDS AND PLOWSHARES

During the dry season in 1923, as the Curtiss "flying boats" of the forest patrol swooped low over the Canadian timberland, their crews alert to any sign of fire, a seven-year-old boy watched in admiration and envy. Often he would wave. From a forward perch in a former gun turret an observer returned the greeting. The more the boy saw of the airborne foresters, the more impressed he became. Soon he began to picture himself as an aviator, in command of powerful aircraft, carrying out important and useful missions. By the time the boy returned several years later to the Michigan Upper Peninsula, the place of his birth, a new goal had crystallized: he would become a test pilot.

By 1943 the young boy's dream had been realized, for now the man was an NACA test pilot flying out of Langley Field and he was flying a Vought F4U Corsair for the first time. Attached to the craft's motor was a hydraulic torquemeter, a device used to monitor and measure engine power. It appeared to be a routine outing, one of many flight tests conducted at Langley during the war years. Suddenly, at 4,000 feet over the nearby town of Newport News, the pressure line connecting the torquemeter to the engine broke. Almost immediately a thick coat of oil streamed along the airplane fuselage and up over the canopy.

To see, the pilot was forced to open the canopy, but in so doing was soon covered in oil himself. His goggles also obscured, the aircraft too slippery for a safe bailout, the pilot

Langley test pilots in 1945, from left, Mel Gough, Herb Hoover, Jack Reeder, Steve Cavallo, and Bill Gray in front of a P-47 Thunderbolt.

NASA Langley photo no. EL-2000-00366

Boeing 737, UH-1H, T38A, BE-80 Queenaire, OV-10A, T-34C, Boeing 757, and F-16XL research aircraft in front of Langley hanger in 1994.

NASA Langley photo no. EL-1996-00055

America's first jet airplane, the Bell YP-59A under test in the Langley Full-Scale Tunnel in 1943.

NASA Langley photo no. EL-2000-00364

decided to return to Langley. As he approached the Field, struggling to see out of one barely open eye, observers said that the plane appeared to be on fire.

As he told this story in the living room of his comfortable Newport News home, John P. (Jack) Reeder, long retired from Langley, smiled at the recollection. The former test pilot survived the brush with catastrophe, flaring his F4U to a safe landing just past the tail of a parked

B-24. "I was not jittery or shocked after it was all over. I was too busy thinking of how to get out of the situation," Reeder recalled. "I really did enjoy my flying, even though I had to handle some pretty wild beasts. Many were unstable—they'd fly sideways, speeds would vary. We'd fly because we were trying to find something wind tunnel tests had not shown. You can not get handling characteristics from a wind tunnel."

The test pilot was the bridge between two ages. If the old aeronautical age was epitomized by the self-sufficient, ingenious individualism of the Wright brothers, then the new aerospace age would be characterized by coordinated group effort between teams of researchers to produce new generations of powerful machines. The challenges posed by flight were becoming more and more complex; no one individual could solve them alone. Humankind was beginning to reach beyond the usual boundaries, beyond the speed of sound, beyond the lower reaches of the atmosphere, even beyond the familiar grasp of Earth's gravity. Highly trained, disciplined, in excellent physical shape, the test pilot would be the point of the human exploratory spear.

The technological explosion that brought the word "aerospace" into use was fueled by the outbreak of World War II. The requirements of that widespread, mechanized war pushed technology to the point where rapid scientific advance came to be taken for granted. Radar, jet aircraft, the atomic bomb, intercontinental ballistic missiles, rockets, computers, communications satellites, and spacecraft: these were but a few of the offspring spawned by a conflict that spanned oceans and continents.

NASA Langley photo no. EL-2000-00370

Technicians installing flaps and wiring on a model around 1944.

NASA Langley photo no. EL-2001-00471

Human "computers" at work in 1947.

For Langley, World War II proved a watershed in several ways. First, the Laboratory's total working staff (professional and nonprofessional) increased by more than 240 percent, from 940 at the end of 1941 to 3,220 by the end of 1945.[1] The pace of technology development accelerated; airplanes were flying faster, higher, and farther. In addition, Langley did not remain NACA's sole research facility. In the late 1930s two additional aeronautical research labs were authorized, Ames Aeronautical Laboratory in Sunnyvale, California, and the Lewis Flight Propulsion Laboratory outside of Cleveland, Ohio. By 1940, Langley had two other NACA Centers with which it shared talent and accumulated experience.[2] While friendly collaboration among the three was the norm, there was also rivalry—tolerated, as *Engineer In Charge* author James Hansen notes, "only to the extent that duplication, competition and cross-fertilization were productive."

War would bring societal change, not the least of which was the increased presence of women in Langley's professional work force. Proportionally speaking, the female presence in engineering science was slight, even though many of Langley's human "computers"—those who assisted engineers by performing mathematical computations by hand on bulky adding-machine-like devices—were women. (This was a fact that pleased some of the Laboratory's male staff who, quite literally, married their computers.)

With the large wartime increase in staff levels, Langley lost some of its clubby, brain-trust feel. Nevertheless, the World War II years and the period following were among Langley's most exciting and productive. In a world where one "hot" war had ended and a "cold" war was about to begin, the question became how to abide by the biblical edict to beat swords into plowshares: that is, how best to adapt machines of war to serve mostly, although not exclusively, peaceful purposes. The answer, at least for those in the aeronautical community, was a full-scale sprint toward jet propulsion and its affiliated technology. Close on the jet's heels were satellite- and human-carrying rockets.

THE SLIPPERY SLOPE

Even as the bloodiest war in human history raged, NACA Langley continued its work in the relative calm of Hampton. During World War II, the Laboratory temporarily shelved basic research and concentrated on immediate goals,

namely the rapid betterment of existing military aircraft design. There was little doubt that improvements were essential. The Germans and Japanese had produced several superb aircraft. In particular, Axis fighters threatened to dominate aerial combat. If the United States and its allies were to emerge victorious, then Allied fighters had to be equally agile and fast.

By the late 1930s, Langley had been called upon by aircraft companies and the military to examine the latest American military airplane prototypes. Over the next several years lives would depend on how fast war planes flew and how efficiently they used fuel. The primary means used to accomplish this was to streamline the entire aircraft surface as much as possible. Drag reduction, or "cleanup," improved considerably military airplane performance. Langley was also called upon to develop the helicopter for search and rescue of military personnel separated from their units during battle.

The Brewster XF2A Buffalo was Langley's first full-fledged effort at drag cleanup. The craft was brought to the Langley Full-Scale Tunnel in April 1938 for study. After five days of intensive tunnel testing, Langley researchers suggested ways to eliminate drag caused by the craft's landing gear, exhaust stacks, machine-gun installation, and gun sight. The proposed changes raised the Brewster's speed to 281 mph from the original 250. The 31-mph boost amounted to more than a ten percent increase in performance.[3]

"We almost took that airplane apart," recollects Herbert A. Wilson, who came to Langley in 1937 and retired as the Center's assistant director for Space in

Brewster Buffalo in Full-Scale Tunnel for drag cleanup studies.

NASA Langley photo no. EL-2001-00379

Grumman F4F Wildcat, later the General Motors FM-2 Wildcat, on the Langley tarmac in 1945.

NASA Langley photo no. EL-2000-00248

Grumman XF6F Hellcat at Langley for turbo-supercharger research beginning in 1944.

NASA Langley photo no. EL-2000-00243

A Lockheed YP-38, a prototype of the Lightning series, in the Full-Scale Tunnel in 1944 for wing investigations.

NASA Langley photo no. EL-2001-00380

1972. "One of the first things we found—and it was very important in World War II—was that the initial cowling design did not pay too much attention to the air flowing through it. Reducing the amount of air flowing into the engine and redirecting it as it flowed out amounted to a significant increase in performance. For one, it cut down on the amount of fuel needed for a given range. For another, it increased the maximum speed."

Extra speed, even as little as a 15-mph edge, could determine the outcome of an aerial dogfight. A faster plane could maneuver behind an opponent and mount a fatal attack. At the beginning of World War II, drag cleanup on the U.S. Navy's front-line fighter, the Grumman F4F Wildcat, made it 45 mph faster. While not the equal of the swifter Japanese Zero, the F4F nonetheless performed well in combat, attaining speeds of up to 320 mph. The F4F's successor, the F6F Hellcat, was faster and more maneuverable, able to reach a maximum speed of 375 mph. The Hellcat, which destroyed nearly 5,000 enemy planes in aerial engagements, is considered by many aviation historians to have been among the best aircraft-carrier-based planes flown by the Navy during World War II.[4]

The Laboratory's meticulous design-analysis efforts spared no detail. Researchers devised one program wherein simulated rivets of varying sizes were mounted, row by row, from the nose backwards, on a series of smooth wings. At each stage the drag caused by the rivets was carefully measured. The results indicated the precise amount of drag induced by a given rivet's size and location. Langley tests indicated that flush, nonprojecting rivets should be routinely used for aircraft to efficiently attain maximum speed.[5]

Similar Langley programs focused on other aircraft components. Modifications were made almost piece by piece. "In the end you knew what percentage of drag was associated with each piece [of the airplane]," says Laurence K. Loftin, Jr., who arrived at Langley in 1944 and retired in 1973 as director for Aeronautics. "The idea was to make airplanes faster. And we did."

The original NACA cowling underwent substantial improvement, as contours were modified to retain low-drag characteristics at speeds approaching 500 mph. Laboratory researchers examined and solved problems with landing gear not properly retracted or fairings that did not properly cover the retracted gear. Some manufacturers failed to correctly smooth the area where the wings joined the airplane fuselage or created poor angles between windshield, canopy, and fuselage, all oversights that resulted in higher-than-necessary drag. These problem areas were also investigated at Langley and solutions were proposed. Researchers also worked to identify basic design flaws, such as the ones that caused a buildup of carbon monoxide in the cockpits of certain U.S. Navy fighters. A poor canopy and fuselage layout allowed the odorless but deadly gas, a by-product of engine combustion, to pass into the pilot compartment.[6]

When late in 1941 the Lockheed P-38 Lightning began to experience problems recovering from high-speed dives, Langley was asked for help. Three months later, after an extensive series of tests in the 8-Foot High-Speed Tunnel,

Dive recovery flaps installed on a P-47 Thunderbolt.

NASA Langley photo no. EL-2001-00456

In 1946 Langley equipped a North American P-51B Mustang with wing gloves to investigate low-drag performance.

NASA Langley photo no. EL-2000-00259

This North American XP-51 Mustang, the second Mustang to serve as a research aircraft, arrived at Langley in 1943.

NASA Langley photo no. EL-2000-00234

Laboratory researchers had devised a dive-recovery flap. Installed on the lower surface of the aircraft wing near the leading edge, the wedge-shaped device created just enough lift so that pilots could regain control. Although a significant wartime contribution in its own right, the flap would also prove useful during Langley's determined research attack on the transonic flight regime, that region where speed increases from just under to just over the speed of sound and where large changes in aerodynamic forces occur. Faster-than-sound flight was only to be achieved after the war, but World War II pilots were already beginning to experience problems related to high aircraft speeds.[7]

Dozens of aircraft passed through the Laboratory for better wartime design and then to combat duty. During one month alone, July 1944, thirty-six U.S. Army and Navy planes were evaluated in detailed studies of stability, control, and performance. Langley tested 137 different airplane types between 1941 and 1945, either in wind tunnels or in flight, including all types that actually saw combat service.[8]

By the late 1930s, a Langley team led by Eastman N. Jacobs had developed a series of airfoils designed to delay the onset of aerodynamic turbulence. As airplanes fly through the atmosphere, air flows over wing surfaces in a series of layers. The layers closest to the wing leading edge are smooth or, in the parlance of aerodynamicists, laminar. But at one point on the wing, depending on design, the smooth flow becomes turbulent as the air layers bunch up and mix together. If it were possible to delay the onset of separation of those air layers and

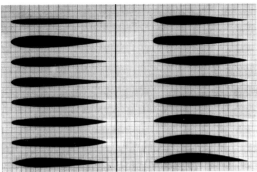

NASA Langley photo no. EL-1999-00372

Several airfoils tested at Langley in 1933.

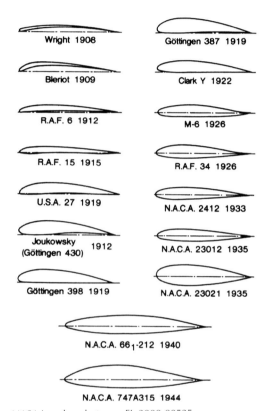

NASA Langley photo no. EL-2000-00525

Historical evolution of airfoil sections.

the drag that resulted, then there would be big payoffs in an airplane's speed, its cruising range, its use of fuel, or combinations thereof.[9]

In Langley's wind tunnels, the so-called laminar-flow airfoils performed well. The air flowing over model wing sections—kept smooth and clean by constant attention—did indeed exhibit laminar-flow properties over a relatively large surface. Test flights, though, were another matter, revealing that true laminar flow was extremely difficult to achieve. Part of the problem was keeping wing surfaces free of debris. The task was next to impossible given the way planes were manufactured—there were plenty of small crevices where dirt could accumulate—and less than ideal given operating conditions—mechanics soiled the aircraft as they maintained or repaired it, and dead insects fouled surfaces on landings and takeoffs. NACA officials ever eager to impress a tight-fisted U.S. Congress with NACA research prowess nevertheless trumpeted the project as a technical triumph.[10]

Although the project was oversold, Langley's laminar-flow efforts did lead to an airfoil-shape series that was first employed on the North American Aviation P-51 Mustang, which first flew in 1941. The Mustang went on to become a highly effective escort fighter for long-range bombing missions in World War II. In fact, this later-named "low-drag series" was so successful in improving aircraft performance, especially at high subsonic speeds, that its airfoil shapes continue to be used by airplane designers.[11]

Some observers have criticized the NACA's wartime efforts as too short-sighted. In this view, while Langley was solving a host of specific war-related problems, equally important fundamental research—notably into jet propulsion and rocketry—went undone. Failure to pursue fundamental research in these areas, some individuals maintain, hindered the Nation's progress in the new field of astronautics. Defenders counter that Langley's wartime focus on improving subsonic military airplanes was proper, indeed essential. "The thought on the part of military planners was to stick with one thing," Herbert Wilson says. "It's for that reason that we were somewhat behind the Germans in rocketry. It was not for lack of imagination on our parts. If we had divided our efforts we might have compromised our ability to win."

As in any victory, however, the attention of the victor must inevitably turn to new conquests. In Langley's case, it was that of passing through an invisible and difficult to understand barrier.

A NEED FOR SPEED

Flying as fast as 100 mph seemed impossible to the pioneer aviators of

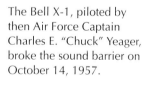

The Bell X-1, piloted by then Air Force Captain Charles E. "Chuck" Yeager, broke the sound barrier on October 14, 1957.

NASA Langley photo no. EL-2001-00386

1910. Thirty-five years later, 100 mph appeared ridiculously slow for everything but recreational flying. During the war years the need for speed was indeed a real one, as pilots sought to outmaneuver and outfight their opponents. Even after—especially after—the cessation of hostilities, fascination with faster and more powerful planes took hold and would not let go.

By the end of World War II, the Germans and the British had a handful of operational jet fighters, and the Americans had begun to fly jet prototypes. In the years between 1948 and 1957, the speed of service fighters in the U.S. Air Force and Navy virtually doubled from 670 to 1,200 mph. A speed faster than that of sound—760 mph at sea level at moderate temperatures, 660 mph at altitudes above 36,000 feet, where temperatures average −60°F— would be attained by Captain Charles E. "Chuck" Yeager on October 14, 1947, in the rocket-propelled X-1. By November 1950, the first jet-to-jet dogfight took place over Korea. In May 1952, scheduled jet passenger service began with the flight of the British-built Comet. By 1954, a prototype of the Boeing 707 had

taken to the air; in that same year, Pan American World Airways ordered 45 jet transports. By the late 1950s, jet transports were routinely flying across the continental United States and to Europe.[12]

The advent of the jet and its penetration into military and commercial spheres would change habits and lives, make a global economy possible in succeeding decades, and spur further aeronautical advances. Although high-speed flight research had been conducted at Langley since the late 1920s, there were enormous technical challenges in making such speeds practical. But the concentrated energies of Langley researchers would, in the 1940s and 1950s, lead to a more complete understanding of high-speed flight. Results of such work at Langley and elsewhere would enable, first, military jets and, later, commercial aircraft to fly at speeds only dreamed of in prior years. In the 1930s Laboratory staff were the first to develop highly efficient airfoil shapes used in the design of high-speed propellers; in the 1940s they were among the first to explore practical methods of traveling beyond the apparent sound barrier.

The effectiveness of a high-speed cowling on this Vought Corsair F4U-1 was examined in the 8-Foot High-Speed Tunnel in 1943.

NASA Langley photo no. EL-2001-00381

Langley researcher
Robert T. Jones.

NASA Langley photo no. EL-2001-00384.

It was in 1938 that British aerodynamicist W. F. Hilton first used the phrase "sound barrier" in remarks made to a reporter. Hilton said that an airplane wing's "resistance" to high speeds "shoots up like a barrier" the closer to the speed of sound an airplane travels.[13]

High flight speeds are often expressed in Mach number multiples, as a tribute to Austrian physicist Ernst Mach, famed for his exploration into the physics of sound. Mach 2, for example, is twice the speed of sound, or 1,320 mph at 36,000 feet or higher.

To fly at supersonic speeds would present vexing challenges, ones that worried designers and engineers alike. Could aircraft be controlled at such high speeds? Would structures survive higher stresses and temperatures? Was supersonic flight at all practical?

"A lot of people thought for years that it was impossible to fly through this sound barrier," observes former aeronautics director Laurence Loftin. "The thought was, if you bump into this invisible wall in the sky your aircraft would go to pieces. Indeed, there was some experimental evidence that this was the case. A number of pilots were killed trying."

The chief difficulty was that of compressibility effects. At near-sonic speeds, more aircraft were subject to a sharp increase in drag and a dramatic decrease in lift. In such extreme circumstances—extreme, that is, compared with subsonic flight—control surfaces of traditional propeller-driven planes did not respond well, if at all. Some pilots in World War II, finding themselves in near-supersonic, fatal dives, literally bent their control sticks in a vain attempt to pull up in level flight. Others—the majority—managed to pull their planes up at lower altitudes.

In 1945 Langley staffer Robert T. Jones was the first American aerodynamicist to realize that the angle at which airplane wings were placed in relation to oncoming air—their sweep—would make a critical difference in achieving and maintaining supersonic flight. Jones' calculations indicated that, at faster-than-sound speeds, the air flowing over a thin sweptback wing would actually be subsonic, thereby delaying or preventing compressibility effects. Swept wings were a significant aeronautical advance and eventually were used on nearly every high performance military airplane. After 1950, wing sweep was also incorporated in the design of commercial aircraft to increase aerodynamic efficiency at high subsonic cruise speeds between Mach 0.8 and 0.85.[14]

For all the desire to get aircraft safely through the sound barrier, the obstacles were formidable. Particularly vexing for wind tunnel researchers was their inability to precisely measure the transonic transformation from pure subsonic to pure supersonic flow. To better understand the nature of the transition, in the mid-1940s researchers employed several methods to collect accurate data. One of the most productive methods involved dropping bomb-like devices containing electronic gear from high flying aircraft.

A Douglas D-558-2 and a
North American F-86
display early examples of
swept wings.

NASA Dryden photo no. E-3996

A small model mounted on
a flight research aircraft to
study supersonic air flow.

NASA Langley photo no. EL-2000-00367

B-29 Superfortress used to
drop test models.

NASA Langley photo no. EL-2001-00385

4

Slotted throat test section installed in
the Langley 8-Foot High-Speed
Tunnel in 1950.

NASA Langley photo no. EL-22000-00280

These "drop bodies" were then tracked by radar. Information on airspeed, readings of atmospheric pressure, temperature, and the like was relayed via a small radio transmitter placed inside the drop body. Many NACA engineers considered these data reliable enough to estimate the drag and power requirements of a future transonic airplane; indeed, test results were incorporated into the design of the sound-barrier-breaking X-1 aircraft.[15]

An earlier method was termed "wing flow technique" and entailed the mounting of a small model wing perpendicular to the wing of a P-51 Mustang. The Mustang took off, flew to altitude, and initiated a series of steep dives. For brief periods during the dives the air would flow supersonically over the model. A small balance mechanism fitted within the P-51's gun compartment and tiny instruments built into the mount of the model recorded the resulting forces and airflow angles.[16]

Still another means of transonic investigation included test runs in the Annular Transonic Tunnel, which, in essence, was a whirling arm with a model attached. There was some question as to the accuracy of the Annular Tunnel data, but it did provide information on airfoil pressure distributions at speeds of Mach 1—the first ever thus collected. In addition, a bump was installed on the floor of the 7- by 10-Foot Tunnel. As air flowed over the bump, on which a small model was attached, the airflow accelerated to transonic velocities even though the main flow remained subsonic.[17]

However ingenious these attempts were, the fact remained that larger scale wind tunnel tests were the preferred method of evaluating the transonic regime. Experiments could be made upon large (even full-scale) models, more accurate information collected, and then repeated to verify initial results. But researchers attempting to increase wind tunnel speeds encountered a phenomenon known as "choking." As airflows increased to near the speed of sound, shock-wave interference patterns would form, thereby skewing the results of tests.[18] Fortunately, a Langley team led by John Stack and Ray H. Wright discovered that the placement of slots along wind tunnel walls reduced or eliminated the interference. The development of this "slotted-throat" wind tunnel was an important advance. Writing with Richard Corliss in *Wind Tunnels of NASA*, Don Baals elaborates on the significance of the find:

Nowhere in the annals of aeronautical history can one find a more convincing argument supporting fundamental research than in the success story of the slotted-wall tunnel. [It was] a breakthrough idea... a long-sought technical prize [which]... ultimately led directly to the discovery of the famous Area Rule, which in turn spawned a whole new generation of aircraft. So important was the slotted wall in aviation research that in 1951 John Stack and his associates at Langley received the coveted Collier Trophy for their work.

Early in 1947 promising test runs of the slotted-throat concept were made in a 12-inch model tunnel. By the end of 1950, the concept was applied to larger facilities as slots were installed in both the 8-Foot and 16-Foot High-Speed Tunnels. Results were, to say the least, encouraging. Initially classified,

The Bell X-1 supersonic airplane in the slotted test section of the 16-Foot High-Speed Tunnel.

NASA Langley photo no. EL-1997-00131

John Stack with a model.

NASA Langley photo no. EL-2000-00372

NACA Flight Test Unit XS-1 team members and USAF pilots. Chuck Yeager is third from the left.

NASA Dryden photo no. E95-43116-5

Test pilots Bill Gray (right) and Jack Reeder with a Bell X-1.

NASA Langley photo no. EL-1996-00242

Langley's slotted-throat breakthrough was made public in the early 1950s, and transonic researchers worldwide quickly altered their wind tunnels to incorporate the modification.[19]

Unique transonic-design, aerodynamic, and propulsion research conducted at Langley was in part responsible for the October day in 1941 when Chuck Yeager briefly broke through the barrier of sound in the rocket-powered X-1, the first of a series of high-speed research aircraft. (The 1947 Collier Trophy went to Yeager, Langley's John Stack, and Bell Aircraft Corporation president Lawrence Bell in recognition of their research accomplishments in faster-than-sound flight.) But Langley had not yet finished its work. There remained a good deal to learn about achieving supersonic flight; breaking the barrier did not mean that aircraft were automatically and immediately able to fly supersonically. The sound barrier was broken by brute force, with rockets, but no aircraft manufacturer in its right mind was going to build commercial or military planes that used high cost, limited-range rockets. Other means would have to be found.

In transonic studies done in the newly modified 8-Foot High-Speed Tunnel, it became apparent that as an airplane approached the speed of sound two different shock waves built up: one on the fuselage and one on the wing trailing edge. It did not appear that conventional designs—the most common was a thick, bullet-like, pointed-nose shape with wings and a tail—would allow an airplane to crack Mach 1. These results were of particular concern to one aircraft manufacturer, Convair, which was building the country's first supersonic fighter-interceptor, the YF-102.[20] Enter Langley researcher Richard Whitcomb with the solution, an idea that thereafter became known as the "area rule."

"We had a transonic wind tunnel and a big drag problem. I was going to use the tunnel to find out what happens to the airflow as it goes around an airplane near or at the speed of sound," says Whitcomb, who began working at Langley in 1943 and who, in 1980, retired as head of the Langley Transonic Aerodynamics Branch. "In 1950 there were no theories to explain it, and yet we had to figure out what was going on. So I collected data and sat there with my feet propped up on my desk and said, 'What the hell's going on?' The shock patterns around the plane were not what you'd expect. There was a shock wave on the wing that came all the way across and hit the fuselage. I had [German aerodynamicist] Adolf Busemann's data in front of me and it suddenly came together, just like the light bulb that lights up in a comic strip.

"The basic idea was to consider the airplane as a whole, a total entity. It can not be looked at as a collection of separate components. That's what the shock wave was telling us. You had to include the whole area. That's where the words 'area rule' came from."

Whitcomb visualized making more room for the air streaming along the fuselage and wings of an airplane about to go supersonic. The shock waves observed in wind tunnel studies were caused by a violent intersection of air and plane. Whitcomb's flash of inspiration: narrow the fuselage in the region of the wing. Air would still be displaced, but not nearly to the extent it otherwise would be. It was a brilliant insight. Soon, aircraft designers would be talking of the "Coke-bottle effect," referring to the

NASA Langley photo no. EL-2001-00388

NASA Langley photo no. EL-2000-00400

Two models of the Convair F-102 sit poised for launch from the Langley Wallops Island facility. Note the application of the area rule on the model in the lower picture.

4

Model of a Bell X-2 in the 9-Inch Supersonic Tunnel in 1947.

NASA Langley photo no. EL-2001-00474

visual consequence of the area rule's application.

Because of its military significance, the area rule proved a national security hot potato, and so was initially kept secret. Its revelation triggered a blizzard of publicity. The National Aeronautic Association awarded Whitcomb the 1954 Collier Trophy, saying, "Whitcomb's area rule is a powerful, simple, and useful method of reducing greatly the sharp increase in wing drag heretofore associated with transonic flight... [and is being used] in the design of all transonic and supersonic aircraft in the United States."

By any standard, the period from 1940 to 1955 had been extraordinary for aeronautics. Langley researchers had a hand in raising aircraft speeds from hundreds to thousands of miles per hour. Emerging from Langley-led research was a historic series of high-speed aircraft, beginning with the sound-barrier-breaking X-1 and continuing with the X-2, X-3, X-4, and X-5. Each aircraft was designed to study different but interre-

lated aspects of high-speed flight. But the Laboratory's accomplishment was not simply the straight-line result of wind tunnel investigations and flight tests under rigorously controlled conditions. Rather, it was the associative power of human intellect and intuition that, combined with an exacting scientific method, enabled fundamental advance.

"Both the slotted tunnel and the area rule derived largely from pictures in the mind," writes James Hansen in *Engineer In Charge*. "Achievements by Langley researchers were products of intelligent guesswork, reasoning by intuition, and cut-and-try testing as much as products of numerical systems analysis, parameter variation, or theory."

The study of the supersonic regime at Langley was but an introduction to even higher speeds. The Laboratory entered into hypersonic research with the hope of understanding and predicting the flight of planes, rockets, and missiles at or above Mach 5. At the time, few realized how close humanity was to the Space Age.

A Langley model maker examines the molds used to make a model of the variable wing sweep Bell X-5.

NASA Langley photo no. EL-2001-003393

FASTER THAN FAST

By late spring of 1944, shortly before D-Day and the Allied invasion of Normandy, even the Nazi High Command realized that the prognosis for Axis victory was poor. In an attempt to recapture the initiative, the Germans unleashed the first of their secret weapons: the "Velgeltungswaffe Ein"—or, in English, "Vengeance Weapon Number One," the world's first cruise missile. The subsonic V-1 and, later, the supersonic V-2 rockets screamed down upon British cities and countryside in what proved to be a vain attempt at intimidation.

One year later, as the "Thousand Year" Reich disintegrated before the relentless Allied onslaught and the advancing armies overran the German rocket-research town of Peenemunde, the true significance of Germany's undeni-

able technological triumph became chillingly clear. Nazi engineers had intended to design long-range ballistic missiles, two of which—the A-9 and A-10—were planned for aerial bombardment of the eastern United States. The Allied discovery of the German rocket-research facility had tremendous psychological impact. If the Germans had succeeded with their ambitious undertaking, World War II might well have had a different outcome. The victorious Allied powers realized full well that no spot, however remote, would be safe from military attack if rockets, wedded to atomic warheads, were only minutes away from delivering their deadly cargo.

Over the next few decades, those countries that could developed their own ballistic missile arsenals to guard against

A one-tenth scale model of the X-15 is prepared for tests in the Langley 7- by 10-Foot Tunnel.

NASA Langley photo no. EL-2001-00420

real or perceived threat. The embrace of rocket technology would make possible humanity's leap into space. It would also create new weapons of mass destruction, thereby altering the course of world military and political history.

Long before World War II, Langley researchers had been aware that jets, missiles, or rockets traveling at high-Mach-number speeds would one day be built. But at that time the problems confronting would-be designers were formidable. Hypersonic speeds appeared too much for even the most advanced aerodynamic devices. Rapid passage through the atmosphere generated an enormous amount of frictional heat, heat well beyond the structural tolerance of most metals or metal alloys. But with speeds in Mach multiples a foregone conclusion, new ways to put missiles or proposed

hypersonic aircraft together had to be considered.

Research on how to do so was undertaken in facilities like the Langley 11-Inch Hypersonic Tunnel, which began operations in the fall of 1947 and was the first of its kind in the United States. Built as a pilot model for a larger hypersonic tunnel—the Continuous-Flow Hypersonic Tunnel, itself built 15 years later—the 11-Inch Tunnel operated for 25 years. In 1973, it was dismantled and given to Virginia Polytechnic Institute and State University in Blacksburg, Virginia, for educational uses. In 1951, another of Langley's hypersonic facilities came online: the Gas Dynamics Laboratory. There, hot, highly pressurized air released in short bursts from huge storage tanks was funneled to test cells to simulate speeds up to Mach 8.[21]

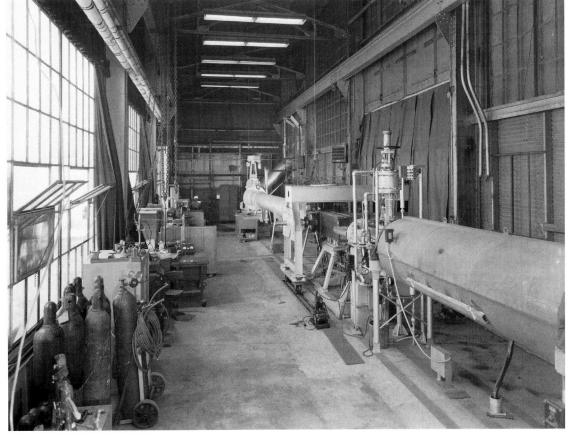

11-Inch Hypersonic Tunnel, which was built in the shop of the Propeller Research Tunnel.

NASA Langley photo no. EL-2000-00265

H. Julian Allen and his blunt body concept.

NASA Ames photo no. A-22664

Hypersonic research at Langley in the late 1940s and early 1950s focused first on the difficulties that long-range missiles would encounter during intercontinental flights. There were many. A successful intercontinental ballistic missile would have to be accelerated to a speed of 15,000 mph at an altitude of 500 miles and then guided to a precise target thousands of miles away. Sophisticated and reliable propulsion, control, and guidance systems were therefore essential, as was the reduction of the missile's structural weight to a minimum. And there was aerodynamic heating, which could cause the missile nose cone to heat up to tens of thousands of degrees Fahrenheit.

The same problems that confronted missile makers would later face spacecraft designers as they attempted to boost a human cargo safely into orbit and return it safely to Earth. The Langley Physical Research Division, which had in the 1940s concentrated on aircraft flutter and vibration problems, took on the materials question. In 1950, the Dynamic Loads Division replaced the Physical Research Division and continued the work that eventually led to successful reentry designs for space capsules.[22]

The aerodynamic heating issue was addressed by former Langley employee H. Julian Allen, who had moved to a new post as chief of High-Speed Research at the NACA Ames Laboratory in California. Allen devised the blunt-body concept, which did away with the idea of a sharply pointed nose in favor of a rounded shape. Upon atmospheric reentry, the blunted form caused the formation of a shock wave, which dissipated most—although not all—of the frictional heat into the atmosphere. Missiles and spacecraft could therefore be made to survive a searing return to Earth. The blunt-body approach was subsequently incorporated into the designs of the

The X-15 launch
techniques were
investigated with a one-
twentieth-scale model.

NASA Langley photo no. EL-2001-00458

Mercury, Gemini, and Apollo astronaut capsules.[23]

The Langley-led X-15 project, a joint effort undertaken by the NACA and the military, was initiated in 1954 to tie together all supersonic research then underway. North American Aviation pilot (and former NACA test pilot) A. Scott Crossfield was at the controls as the X-15, the first hypersonic research airplane, undertook its maiden flight on June 8, 1959. In investigations intended to gather data on aerothermodynamics, structures, flight controls, and human physiological reactions to high-speed, high-altitude flights, three X-15s flew a total of 199 missions between June 1959 and October 1968.[24] Perhaps most important, the X-15 served as the test bed for techniques and systems that later would be employed in the development of the Space Shuttle. As author James Hansen writes:

The Shuttle's reentry characteristics—the transition from the reaction controls used in space to aerodynamic controls, the use of high angles of attack to keep the dynamic pressures and the heating problems within bounds, and the need for artificial damping and other automatic stability and control devices to aid the pilot—are similar in all important respects to those of the X-15 conceived at Langley.

Until the first orbital flight of the Space Shuttle *Columbia* in 1981, the X-15 held the altitude and speed records for winged aircraft, with flights as high as 67 miles and a maximum speed of 6.7 times the speed of sound or 4,518 mph. The X-15 program was, agree the experts, one of the most successful aeronautical research endeavors ever undertaken.

"Some have said that the X-15 was the hyphen in aerospace," says John Becker, retired chief of the High-Speed

Aerodynamics Division. "Up until 1952 or '53, there was almost no realization that we were on the verge of the Space Age. Then, suddenly, we realized we had the propulsion to get up to hypersonic speeds and also to get out of the atmosphere—at least for a while—and out into space. When that began to sink in, it became a very exciting period."

SPUTNIK SHOCK

Alone among the four major Allied powers, the infrastructure of the United States emerged unscathed from World War II. Protected from sustained attack by two vast oceans, the United States had not suffered the terrible devastation experienced in Europe and Asia. Its industrial base vigorous, America prospered, becoming the world's most powerful nation. By the time Dwight Eisenhower became the 34th president in January 1953, and despite fears of Communist infiltration or aggression sponsored by the Soviet Union, American technological dominance was taken for granted. So it was a profound shock when the Soviet Union beat the United States into space on October 4, 1957, with the launch of the first satellite, *Sputnik*. To add insult to injury, less than a month later, on November 3, the Soviet Union sent into orbit another satellite. *Sputnik 2* carried a payload many times heavier than the tiny

payload planned for *Vanguard*, the first American satellite.

Renowned American scientific and technological know-how suddenly seemed second best, overshadowed by an ascendant Communist space science. The beep-beep-beep of the orbiting Soviet satellite took on ominous overtones and was amplified by national doubt and embarrassment until it reverberated across the political landscape like the characteristic boom produced by an airplane going supersonic. Scarcely a year after the *Sputnik* scare, the NACA was no more—replaced by another agency, NASA, whose implicit priority was to make America number one in space. It had not been too long before, as one observer dryly commented, that the NACA stood "as much chance of injecting itself into space activities in any real way as an icicle had [surviving] in a rocket combustion chamber."

At first, things did not go smoothly as the United States played space catch-up. James Hansen explains:

... On the sixth of December [1957], with hundreds of reporters from all over the world watching, the Vanguard *rocket rose a mere four feet off its pad at Cape Canaveral, toppled over, and erupted into a sea of flames. The international press dubbed the failed American*

The X-15 held the world altitude and speed records for winged flight until the first flight of Space Shuttle *Columbia*.

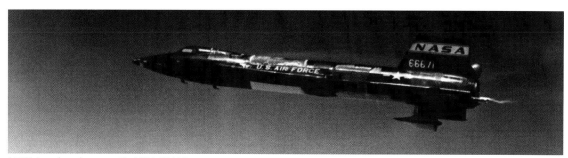

NASA Langley photo no. EL-2001-00429

satellite "Kaputnik" and "Stayputnik."
Cynical and embarrassed Americans
drank the Sputnik cocktail: two parts
vodka, one part sour grapes.

At the United Nations, a Soviet dele-
gate even asked sarcastically if the
United States would receive aid as an
underdeveloped country. But the ridicule
was short-lived. Six weeks later, on
January 31, 1958, an Army team headed
by former German rocket scientist
Wernher von Braun managed a successful launch of the 31-pound *Explorer 1*.
At long last, America was in space.

Nationally, changes in aerospace-
related government policy were under
way. One of the biggest came in the
changeover from NACA to NASA management. Although certainly not a major
change in the eyes of employees—nearly
everyone retained the same job and
responsibilities—over time, the transformation would prove significant. NASA
would undertake projects on a scale
unheard of in NACA days. As perceived
masters of space technology, the new
agency would also be held to standards
few (if any) government agencies could
easily match. Every NASA success was
lauded, every shortcoming mercilessly
scrutinized. Whether for good or ill, the
NACA had rarely, if ever, been put under
such a powerful public microscope.

In Langley's case a more local
transformation involved the public perception of the "Nacka nut." No longer
considered technology-obsessed eccentrics, Langley research scientists and
engineers were becoming Space Age
wizards, valued as interpreters of the
obscure runes of spaceflight physics and
orbital mechanics.

NASA Marshall photo no. MSFC-0100074

Launch of *Explorer 1* on a
Jupiter-C rocket.

"Conjure the scene from *The Wizard
of Oz*: the wicked witch flies over the
Emerald City spelling out 'Surrender
Dorothy,'" James Hansen writes, "and all
the terrified citizens rush to the wizard to
find out what it means. In an exaggerated
way, this gives some idea of how the
Sputnik crisis and the resulting American
space program triggered the local public's feelings of wonder about, and admiration for, Langley."

As the first home to the U.S. human
space flight program and the first NASA
astronaut training center, Langley
Research Center would prove that it
could learn as much about the practicali-
ties of spaceflight as it already had about
the requirements of aircraft flight.

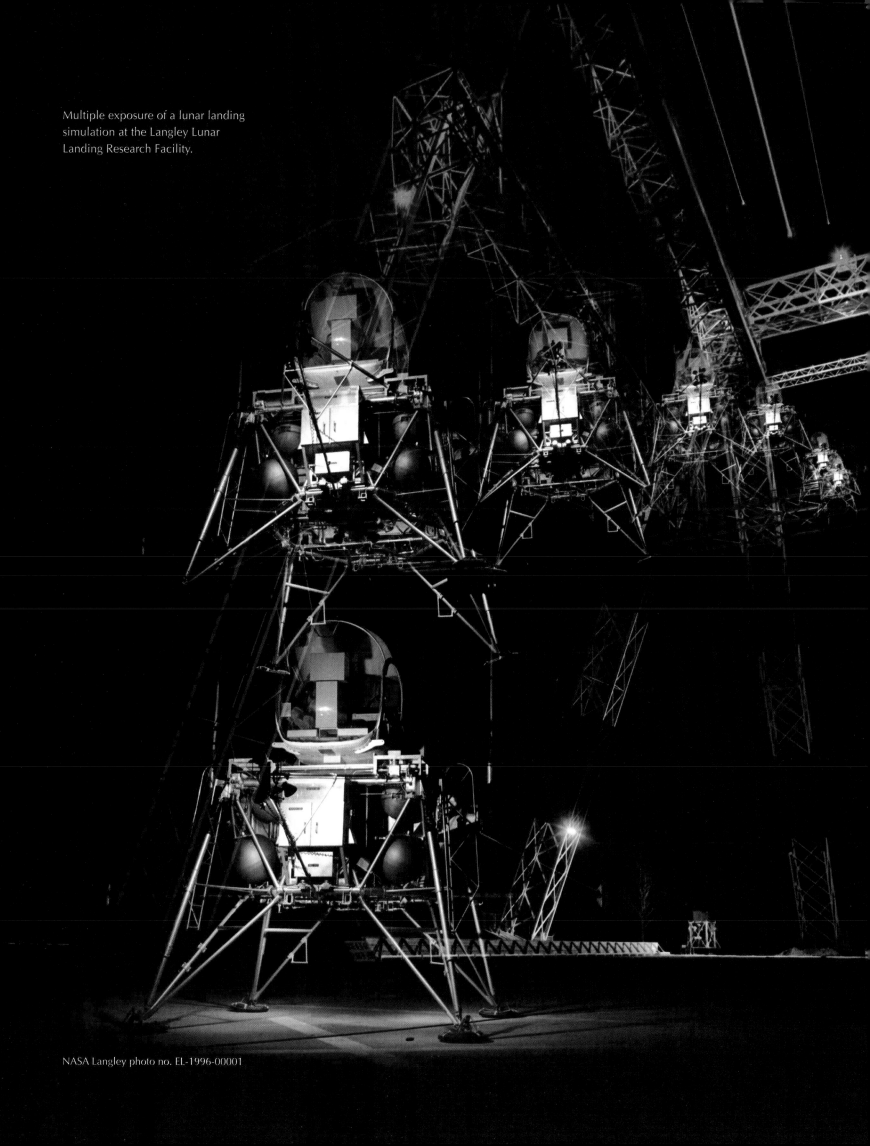

Multiple exposure of a lunar landing
simulation at the Langley Lunar
Landing Research Facility.

NASA Langley photo no. EL-1996-00001

5

BEYOND THE HOME PLANET

Something about a beach soothes the soul. The rhythm of seawater falling on sand, the nearly constant wind, and the sight of a vast ocean vanishing over the horizon relaxes and comforts. For the Wright brothers, an oceanside test site was eminently practical: steady winds could keep research gliders aloft for many minutes. Landing on sand would also prove gentler on the flimsy structure of the Wright *Flyer.* Also, the Wrights could carry on their work far from the prying eyes of the press.

For a later generation engaged in rocket research, surf side was also the place to be. The secluded Wallops Island range where Langley began testing rocket models in the mid-1940s suited NACA officials just fine, especially since, as part of its overall program, the Laboratory was providing research assistance to the military for a highly classified guided-missile program. In addition, working on the island kept inherently dangerous devices away from population centers. In the event of explosion or in-flight destruction, it was far better to have a rocket break up over the ocean than over a city. Not that Langley researchers wanted to see their work go up in smoke. On the contrary, successful research-rocket firings from Wallops would furnish much useful information, information that in time would prove invaluable in the American exploration of the high frontier of space.

By 1944, small teams of Langley Wallops Island researchers were launching rocket models that weighed about 40 pounds. Instruments placed inside relayed information via

Project engineer Sidney Alexander adjusts a typical RM-2 model in its special launcher at Wallops Island in 1945.

NASA Langley photo no. EL-2000-00258

The launching of the first rocket at the NACA's Wallops Island Facility on June 27, 1945.

NASA Langley photo no. EL-1996-00254

radio signals to observers on the ground. Although the results helped to further the U.S. Army ballistic missile experiments, NACA researchers were keenly interested in defining the best airplane wing-and-fuselage configuration and control systems to fly in and through the transonic range. Rocket-model tests helped to improve high-speed research methods and devices. Langley scientists and engineers developed new ways of measuring, transmitting, and recording accurate data even as their small rockets changed speed, altitude, and attitude in a matter of a few seconds.[1]

For the individuals working at Wallops in the 1940s and 1950s, Eastern Shore isolation created a sense of fellowship, in part because of the rugged surroundings. The island was difficult to reach; once there, researchers could expect to stay as long as six months. Housing was primitive, a choice of spartan prefabricated metal huts or, for the adventuresome, tents pitched on the beach. Food was plentiful and good, but entertainment was limited. There was a shortwave radio to listen to, card games after dinner, spirited conversation, and the camaraderie of the like-minded. All in all, report former Wallops rocketeers, it was one of the most enjoyable experiences of their lives.

After the Wallops complex was administratively transformed in June 1946 into a separate Langley division, it began to attract attention from other Laboratory departments because of the sheer number of models sacrificed in the name of science. In the period from 1947 to 1949, more than 380 plunged to a watery grave in the Atlantic Ocean. Langley wind tunnel personnel complained that such an expenditure was

Crafting Flight

roughly equivalent to the requirements of 10 major wind tunnels. Wallops rocketeers countered that one single rocket-model test, because it provided important aerodynamic data, was comparable to the dollar-for-dollar return from wind tunnel research.[2]

Whatever the technical or other merits, those working at Wallops were energized by their labors. "The environment at that time was something. I remember thinking, 'You pay people to do this?'" recounts W. Ray Hook, former Langley director for Space. "There was great freedom to make mistakes. People did not fear trying something new. The attitude was, if you think you can do it, try it. We were flying things on rockets at a good clip fairly early in our careers. And we built nearly everything ourselves. You got your own model, assembled your team, lit the fuse, and graded your 'paper' in front of God and everybody. It was tremendous sport."

Not every rocket went off according to intent. Some experiments had to be rethought even though the basic premise appeared sound. Once, investigators had to scrap plans to send a pig on a 100,000-foot suborbital flight. Although researchers had gone to the trouble of designing a special couch for their would-be porcine passenger, it was determined that pigs can die if they lie on their backs for too long. But an animal finally did make it into space from Wallops. On December 4, 1959, a successful suborbital test of the Mercury capsule boosted Sam, a rhesus monkey, to an altitude of about 53 miles.[3]

One important project that was initiated in the late 1950s at Wallops was the Solid Controlled Orbital Utility Test Program, otherwise known as Scout. The program officially began in 1957 with the stated intent of building an inexpensive sounding rocket to carry small research payloads to high altitudes. In May 1958, those goals were further refined: Scout

A five-stage missile-research rocket takes off from Wallops Island in 1957.

would be a four-stage solid-fuel booster capable of placing a 150-pound satellite into an orbit 500 miles above Earth. On February 16, 1961, Scout successfully boosted into orbit the *Explorer 9* satellite, a 12-foot sphere designed for atmospheric-density measurements. Scout thus became the first solid-rocket booster to lift a payload into orbit, and the first vehicle to do so from Wallops Island.

Scout would eventually assist the Mercury, Gemini, and Apollo programs by testing reentry materials, evaluating methods of protecting spacecraft from micrometeoroids, and examining ways of overcoming radio blackouts as a space capsule reentered the atmosphere. The Department of Defense used Scout to launch the U.S. Navy's highly successful Transit navigation satellites, which pass 600 miles overhead every 80 minutes broadcasting positioning information used by warships, fishing vessels, pleasure craft, cars, and hand-held devices. For the Air Force, Scout launched in-space targets that were used to test anti-satellite weapons fired from F-15 fighters. Scout scientific payloads also examined how water vapor and other aerosols have affected Earth's atmosphere, mapped the planetary magnetic field, and made the first observations of a suspected black hole at the center of a collapsed star.

"I do not think there's ever been another project where government and contractor personnel worked together as closely as they did on Scout," says former Scout Project Manager Roland English. "Partly, I guess, it was the nature of the program. The goal we had, the job we were charged to do, [was make] an inexpensive rocket that could be used by a lot of people. It was a goal you could put your heart into."

Designing, building, and flying rockets was—and is—not an easy endeavor. As in any complicated undertaking, perseverance can make the difference between success and failure. Langley rocket researchers kept at it and in the process accumulated valuable experience that could not be gained in any but the school of hard knocks. The skills of Wallops' rocketeers would be put to a bigger test as the United States took its first steps across the borders of the space frontier.

TO THE MOON BY NOON?

On July 29, 1958, President Dwight Eisenhower signed legislation that would spell the end of one federal agency and mark the beginning of another. In remarks made at the signing, Eisenhower said that "the present National Advisory Committee for Aeronautics with its large and competent staff and well-equipped laboratories will provide the nucleus for NASA.... The coordination of space-exploration responsibilities with NACA's traditional aeronautical research functions is a natural evolution...." That evolution was finalized on October 1, 1958, when the NACA officially became the National Aeronautics and Space Administration.

The substitution of the "C" in NACA with the "S" of NASA (or, as some pundits suggested, the replacement of a cents sign with a dollar sign, referring to the higher cost of bigger projects) did not at first seem likely to cause much of an uproar at Langley. After all, those who left work on Tuesday evening,

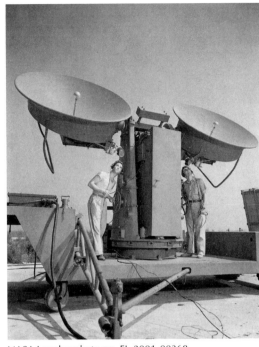

The first Scout (left) launched at Wallops Island July 1, 1960.

Doppler radar (right), which allowed determination of velocity and the measurement of drag of rockets, at Wallops Island.

NASA Langley photo no. EL-2001-00445

NASA Langley photo no. EL-2001-00368

Launch Area 3 on Wallops Island where Scout rockets were launched.

NASA Langley photo no. EL-2001-00446

Technicians prepare prototype of Mercury space capsule in 1959.

NASA Langley photo no. EL-1996-00069

September 30, 1958, as NACA employees were the same people who would
come to work as NASA employees
Wednesday morning, October 1. But the
transformation was unsettling, at least in
a long-term sense. For Langley, the
change spelled the true end—the first
phase of which was the large-scale
expansion during World War II—of the
small-scale, tightly knit brain trust that
had concentrated on specific aeronautical
problems since the Laboratory's formation in 1917. There was also a name
change: to the NASA Langley Research
Center.

The degree of project difficulty
would increase as well. The requirements
of space travel, crewed and uncrewed,
presented unprecedented challenge. The
ranks of middle-level management grew,
aided by the need to organize and carry
out large-scale programs.

In the span of a few years, NASA's
entire effective work force included thousands of outside contractors hired to
assist in research and to build the complex machines that would chart and
travel the solar system. But perhaps the
most significant effect of the NACA-to-
NASA transition, seen most clearly in
the new agency's large-scale space effort,
was on the public imagination. Generally
speaking, the public idolized NASA, seeing its scientists and engineers as heroes
and high-tech warriors doing great deeds
in a new age. NASA became the one
government agency that could do little
wrong, in the race to put Americans into
space.

A few of Langley's aeronautical
engineers, enthusiastic about all things
related to flight, were dismayed by the
newfound dedication to space. Some

A model of the Mercury
space capsule during
flotation tests.

NASA Langley photo no. EL-2001-00421

Mercury space capsule in
the Langley Full-Scale
Tunnel for tests.

NASA Langley photo no. EL-1996-00094

would opt for retirement or seek employment in the private sector. Others stayed,
but felt that the space race was nothing
more than political posturing, (one prominent Langley staffer was contemptuous
of what he called "to-the-Moon-by-
noon" philosophy). Still others gave
newborn NASA its grudging due, but
more out of loyalty to the NACA technological track record. In any event, when
President John F. Kennedy declared in a
May 26, 1961, speech before Congress
that before the decade was out Americans
would land on the Moon, there did not
seem to be a shortage of doubters.

"Two years after the Apollo program was announced, in 1963, I had lunch with two Langley division chiefs," John Becker relates. "They said that Apollo was the most dishonest thing to ever happen in the aerospace industry. They said it was crazy to embark upon a project we know we can not do. I sat there and listened to a long litany of problems. But I was thinking, 'Most of us are engineers trained in the old-fashioned way. We have a lot of new things to learn.'"

New things learned would blur an already fuzzy line between matters relating to aircraft and those regarding space travel. There were various degrees of technical and administrative separation between the two areas, but often the very people working on spacecraft had wrestled with the transonic problem, or fretted over issues regarding aircraft instrumentation, or were laboring to improve

an aircraft's structural integrity. In practical terms, this meant that most Langley engineers would move with ease from working on aeronautics problems one day to addressing space-travel difficulties the next.

Confident in their own abilities, proud of the NACA's achievements, most NASA researchers were sure they could put American spacecraft into orbit. But they were used to relatively small-scale endeavors. Could NASA carry off its expanded mission with the same skill that the NACA had expressed in admittedly more limited arenas? Former NASA engineer Richard E. Horner, in a May 1972 interview, outlined some of the management problems NASA encountered: "The NACA cadre had the typical technical man's disease at the time: the virus of wanting to do too much, the 'reach exceeds my grasp'

John H. Glenn performs a training exercise in the Mercury Procedures Trainer at Langley.

GRIN photo no. GPN-2002-000044

problem. When I first joined NASA in June of 1959, I was just flabbergasted at the number of programs that were being attempted.... It was very clear to me that either we were not going to get anything done on schedule, or we were going to have to eliminate an awful lot of things that we were trying to do in the process.... In making the transition [from NACA to NASA] some management mistakes were made. On the other hand, the way the program evolved, they were able to bridge the management-experience gap very successfully."

An in-house researcher-led program at Langley that aimed to put astronauts in space as soon as possible led directly to the formation, in August 1958, of the Space Task Group (STG). Comprised of Langley rocket-research veterans and others from various Langley divisions, as well as personnel from then Lewis, now Glenn, Research Center in Ohio, the STG was the 36-person nucleus around which the entire U.S. human space flight program ultimately condensed. Researchers well-known to insiders—such as Max Faget, Robert Gilruth, Caldwell Johnson, and Christopher Kraft—were among the handful of leaders responsible for mounting the successful U.S. assault on space. At the time of the STG's formation, most of these individuals were working at Langley. Langley would remain the STG headquarters site until the formation of the Johnson Space Center in 1962.[4]

Even before the Space Task Group was formally organized, the Langley members had begun to develop the concept of the "Little Joe" test vehicle, which became the workhorse of the Mercury program. In pre-STG days, Center researchers had also

NASA Langley photo no. EL-2000-00412

The "Little Joe" test vehicle being readied for launch from Wallops in 1960.

NASA Langley photo no. EL-1996-00068

The "Little Joe" ascends on a plume of exhaust.

For Project FIRE, technicians ready materials for a high temperature test to simulate reentry heating (shown on the left).

Preparing Project FIRE model capsules to be sent aloft on ballistic missiles (shown on the right).

NASA Langley photo no. EL-2000-00427

NASA Langley photo no. EL-2001-00395

Echo I was the first U.S. passive communications satellite.

NASA Langley photo no. EL-2001-00369

demonstrated the feasibility of a crewed satellite program by using existing ballistic missiles as launch vehicles, and originated the contour couch concept, which was adopted for use in all subsequent U.S. space flights. Once it crystallized, the STG began to address additional technical issues, among them proof of the feasibility of a heat-dissipating shield for astronaut-carrying capsules and the

development of astronaut "procedure trainers," later called simulators.

A number of Langley-based programs were assigned to support the work of the task group. One such was Project FIRE (Flight Investigation Reentry Environment), which investigated the intense heat (several thousands of degrees Fahrenheit) of atmospheric reentry and its effects on would-be spacecraft materials such as copper, tungsten, Dupont Teflon® material, nylon, and fiberglass.

Building test facilities to simulate such extreme heat was no small technical feat, and Langley engineers relied on several different types of technology. One involved the heating, to 4,400°F, of a bed of pebbles made from the metallic element zirconium. Another method created a brief but intense flame from the action of an electric charge upon a compressed test gas. A third involved the launch of multistage sounding rockets from Wallops, a means by which reentry speeds as high as Mach 26 were attained.

In this same time period, Project RAM (Radio Attenuation Measurements) focused on how to transmit radio waves through the plasma sheath that formed around spacecraft reentering the atmosphere. Also undertaken was Project Echo, which led to development of the Nation's first passive communications satellite. Made from aluminized Dupont Mylar™ plastic, the 100-foot-diameter *Echo I* was a giant, automatically inflated balloon off which radio signals could be bounced. Launched on August 12, 1960, into an equatorial orbit approximately 1,000 miles high, *Echo I* could be seen with the naked eye—a graphic reminder of the American effort to effectively compete with the Soviet Union in space.[5]

Of the many notable achievements of the early years of the Space Task Group, one of the most important was the establishment of the Mercury Tracking Network. For the first time, spacecraft and their human operators were to be actively monitored while in orbit. By any standard, it was a gargantuan and unprecedented undertaking. Organized and managed out of Langley, the tracking network's successful implementation

NASA Headquarters photo no. 64-H-2487

Melba Roy headed the group of NASA mathematicians, known as "computers," who tracked the *Echo* satellites.

NASA Langley photo no. EL-2000-00409

Mercury capsule model in Langley Spin Tunnel.

underscored that the Center engineers had what writer Tom Wolfe would later characterize as "the right stuff."

The work of the STG was absolutely essential to the U.S. space effort. The STG later left Langley to found the Johnson Space Center in Houston and to oversee the Gemini and Apollo projects, but its early work in Hampton set the standards by which subsequent U.S. space success was made possible. Heirs to the NACA problem-solving tradition, the STG made it clear to anyone who would listen that exploration of space and flights to the Moon were no longer in the realm of science fiction.

"No Albert Einstein was required. Everything we did at the time was doable," says Israel Taback, who upon his retirement in 1976 was chief engineer on Project Viking, the Mars exploration program. "We understood trajectories. Developing new boosters, new spacecraft, coming up with rendezvous techniques—it was basically an enormous engineering challenge. The only intimidating thing was the size of the job: thousands and thousands of people working all over the country to put two men

on the surface of the Moon. Langley was sort of the parent university."

STILL UP IN THE AIR

However preoccupied NASA was in the 1960s with space-related matters, at Langley aeronautics research continued. Much had been accomplished in the previous decade, particularly where subsonic flight was concerned. Langley's aeronautics work in the late 1950s and 1960s began to include a focus on supersonic transport technologies.

One such area involved the concept of the variable-sweep wing. Simply put, the notion was a variation of swept-wing theory with this refinement: an airplane's wings could be mechanically adjusted to different sweep angles to conform to either sub- or supersonic flight. At times of takeoff, climb to altitude, and landing, the wings ideally would extend almost at

One-tenth scale model of a variable wing F-111A being readied for a wind tunnel test.

NASA Langley photo no. EL-2001-00477

right angles to the fuselage, or "near-zero" sweep. When flying faster than the speed of sound, the airplane would resemble the head of a spear or an arrow, as its wings would be fully swept back.

Although first identified in the early to mid-1950s as a potential means of improving a military airplane's operating efficiency, variable sweep as an application proved difficult. Tests made on variable-sweep models indicated that they all suffered from major—and in the real world, deadly—changes in stability as the wings were rotated through various angles. Langley-led studies indicated that properly positioning the point at which the wings pivoted would provide the needed stability; it was a notable advance.

To validate the discovery, Langley researchers built four scale models and tested them at transonic speeds in the 8-Foot Transonic Pressure Tunnel. Free-flight model tests were also made. Sweep angles were varied from 25 to 75 degrees and no significant problems, either of stability or control, were observed. One of the most astonishing things about the venture was its speed: Project Hurry Up took little more than two weeks from start to finish. As a direct result of the Langley tests, in 1961 the Defense Department gave the go-ahead for production of the Nation's first variable-sweep fighter, the F-111. Built by General Dynamics, the F-111 first flew in 1964 and entered operational service in 1967. It has retired from U.S. service, but is still operated by the Australian Air Force. Variable sweep was subsequently incorporated in the design of many of the fleet of advanced U.S. military aircraft.

A tilt-wing prototype used in vertical takeoff and landing studies.

NASA Langley photo no. EL-2001-00399

Langley's first vertical takeoff and landing model in 1950.

NASA Langley photo no. EL-2001-00442

A duct-fan method of propulsion was tested with wind tunnel models like this one.

NASA Langley photo no. EL-2001-00447

Smoke flow visualization shows the flow of air around model air foil at 100 feet per second.

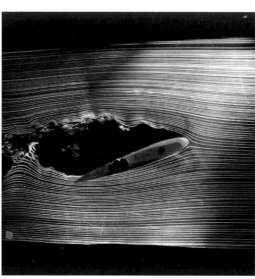

NASA Langley photo no. EL-2001-00461

Also under research scrutiny at Langley in the 1960s were gust alleviation, active boundary-layer control, and vertical/short takeoff and landing (V/STOL) systems. Protecting against turbulence caused by wind gusts was of particular concern to the Air Force, which was relying on low-flying bombers as part of its strategic plan in case of war. As a result of tests conducted at Langley in the late 1950s and early 1960s, structural modifications were made to one model series of the B-52 bomber. (The commercial aircraft industry found little use for the concept.)

An active boundary-layer control system was installed on a prototype Boeing 707-80 airplane in 1964. Large quantities of air were injected parallel to the wing surface and over the leading edge of the flaps to increase the amount of lift at low speeds. The demonstration proved that safe landings could be made with more efficient use of the aircraft power-plant and speed-control systems.

Building on autogyro research that began in the late 1920s and reached substantial levels during the final years of World War II, Langley undertook evaluation of a variety of V/STOL approaches in the 1960s. V/STOL designs permitted aircraft to rise vertically, helicopter-like, and then fly horizontally. In following years, these designs would be further refined, with the goal of producing a short-hop commuter aircraft. A V/STOL craft needs less runway area in which to operate, which may be useful in easing chronic airport congestion that is predicted to worsen. The V/STOL technology is used in the Harrier jump jet, deployed by the U.S. Marines on aircraft carriers. While seemingly ideally suited to business transportation, the

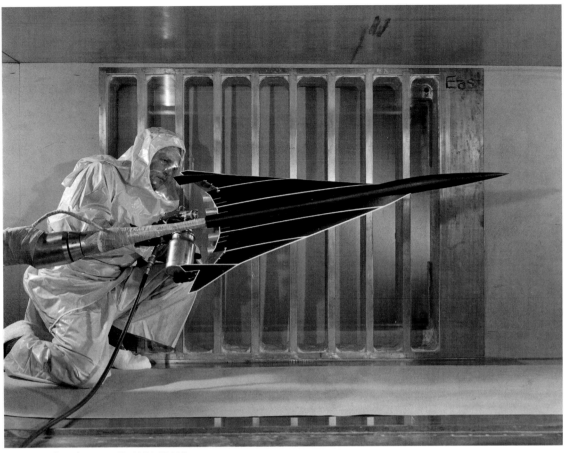

Supersonic Commercial Air Transport (SCAT) model in Langley Unitary Plan Wind Tunnel.

NASA Langley photo no. EL-2001-00425

Model of a supersonic transport (SST) variable-sweep version prior to tests in the Full-Scale Tunnel.

NASA Langley photo no. EL-2001-00452

Richard Whitcomb examines a model incorporating his supercritical-wing concept.

NASA Langley photo no. EL-2001-00478

A SCAT model awaits aerodynamic evaluation.

NASA Langley photo no. EL-2001-00400

technology's reliability and overall cost remain issues. Nevertheless, Langley researchers continued to evaluate V/STOL designs as requested by aircraft manufacturers.

By the 1960s, Langley's area rule originator Richard Whitcomb had made another discovery, this one related to the shape of an airplane wing. Whitcomb was looking for ways to delay the onset of the high wing drag caused by localized supersonic flow occurring at high subsonic speeds. Since the basic airfoil shape was responsible, in his mind's eye Whitcomb visualized an alternative: a wing with a flat top and curved bottom. This "supercritical" wing—supercritical referring to that speed at which a large amount of drag is first encountered by an airplane traveling near Mach 1—delayed the formation of shock waves. The supercritical concept, when applied to thicker airfoils, results in no drag increase relative to thinner airfoils at high subsonic speeds. As a result of this aerodynamic advantage, designers could use the thicker airfoils to build more efficient structural wing designs. The practical result of the adoption of the supercritical wing was an increase in performance— improved fuel efficiency and greater range. The advance was quickly adopted by commercial airlines. Although incorporation of supercritical wings can increase speed, nearly all commercial airlines have used the design to improve performance, thereby decreasing operating costs.

In retrospect, a significant focus of the aeronautical effort at Langley in the 1960s was research into a supersonic transport, or SST. After Langley X-15

studies, it appeared as though an X-20— a so-called Dyna-Soar (Dynamically Soaring Vehicle)—might be built to operate at speeds in excess of Mach 7 and that Langley would play a primary role in its development. But the Dyna-Soar project was canceled in 1963.

In 1959, as part of a joint NASA and Federal Aviation Administration effort, Langley had undertaken an SST technology-development program known as the Supersonic Commercial Air Transport program, or SCAT. The aim of the SCAT studies was to identify ways in which a commercial supersonic transport could become part of the daily lives of American airplane passengers as subsonic aircraft had.

The array of imperatives facing SST designers was intimidating. The SST would have to be structurally sound, fuel-efficient, cost-effective, have a cruising speed of between Mach 2 and Mach 3, and not harm the environment. These difficult-to-meet and competing requirements were, ultimately, to prove too much for the then-current level of aeronautical technology to overcome, particularly in light of the ensuing political debate that sharply questioned the need for an American SST. In late May 1971, the U.S. Congress canceled the program, citing high cost of use, operational problems, and environmental concerns.

Nevertheless, the effort brought together for the first time a number of space-age technologies: new metal alloys, new approaches to structural design, new engines, computer-controlled instrumentation, and computer-driven aircraft-design and environmental-impact modeling. In one

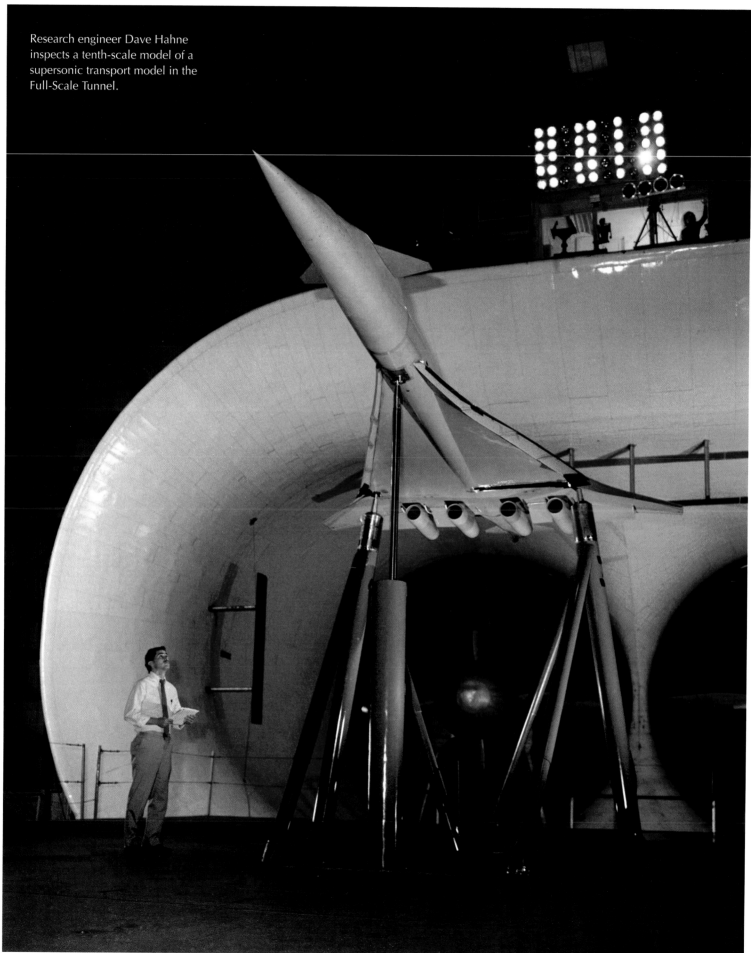

Research engineer Dave Hahne inspects a tenth-scale model of a supersonic transport model in the Full-Scale Tunnel.

NASA Langley photo no. EL-1996-00008

sense, the SST program confirmed the importance of the interdisciplinary approach to airplane design, a trend that has intensified with the passage of time.

Five years after the American SST program was abolished, the British-French Concorde became the world's first commercial supersonic transport in regular service. An undeniable triumph of late 1960s engineering, the Mach 2 Concorde is still flying but has never turned a profit, limited as it is by passenger-carrying capacity, high operating cost, and restricted landing rights.

Shortly after the SST cancellation, Langley was directed to put its supersonic and hypersonic technology efforts into hibernation. That the Center kept the research alive (if barely) was tribute to the stubborn foresight that 20 years later would come in handy as the Nation thought once again about propelling ordinary citizens faster than the speed of sound.

MOON MATTERS

As Project Mercury began in the late 1950s, Langley was thrust full force into the national spotlight with the arrival in Hampton of the original seven astronauts. Under the tutelage of the Space Task Group, Scott Carpenter, Gordon Cooper, John Glenn, Virgil "Gus" Grissom, Walter Schirra, Alan Shepard, and Donald "Deke" Slayton were trained to operate the space machines that would thrust them beyond the protective envelope of Earth's atmosphere.

The locals took keen note of Langley's astronaut-induced prominence. When Mercury proved successful, and ultimately evolved into Project Apollo, respect for the Center grew even greater, especially among the young. Adults, too, were caught up in the wave of enthusiasm. Hamptonians were so pleased with the attention that the space programs were bringing to their city that

NASA Langley photo no. EL-1996-00070

The original seven Mercury astronauts, from left front row: Virgil "Gus" Grissom, Scott Carpenter, Donald "Deke" Slayton and Gordon Cooper; back row: Alan Shepard, Walter Schirra and John Glenn trained at Langley until the Space Task Group moved to Houston.

5

Multiple exposure of the Langley Rendezvous and Docking Simulator used to train Gemini astronauts.

NASA Langley photo no. EL-1999-00385

A full-scale model of the Gemini capsule in the Langley Rendezvous and Docking Simulator.

NASA Langley photo no. EL-2001-00397

Practicing lunar orbit rendezvous with an Apollo capsule in the Langley Rendezvous and Docking Simulator.

NASA Langley photo no. EL-2000-00439

they voted to change the name of Military Highway to Mercury Boulevard and to dedicate the town's bridges in honor of the astronauts. Hampton and the United States had found new champions.

The Soviet Union, meanwhile, was moving forward determinedly with its space program. On April 12, 1961, cosmonaut Yuri Gagarin soared into a 108-minute orbit aboard the 5-ton Vostok rocket, thus officially becoming the first man to orbit Earth. Three days later, the world's attention was refocused on Earth, as the U.S.-led Bay of Pigs invasion of Cuba was repulsed by soldiers loyal to Fidel Castro. Following that event, President John Kennedy sought to repair the damage done to the national prestige and his own political fortunes by intensifying American commitment to space flight. The result: the end-of-May 1961 speech during which the U.S. lunar mission was proclaimed.

Now that such an ambitious goal had been defined, the question was whether or not the United States could engineer its way to the Moon. Suborbital, even orbital, flights were doable. But by what method would a lunar landing be accomplished?

To meet President Kennedy's end-of-decade deadline, NASA considered three separate options. First studied was direct ascent, followed by Earth-orbit rendezvous (EOR), and finally, lunar-orbit rendezvous (LOR). Direct ascent involved the launch of a battleship-size rocket from Earth to the Moon and back again—basically the method popularized in Hollywood movies and science fiction novels. EOR entailed launching two spacecraft into Earth orbit, the payloads of which would be assembled into

a vehicle that could travel to the Moon and then back to Earth.

The third choice was considered a dark-horse candidate. According to the LOR concept, three small spacecraft—a command module, a service module (with fuel cells, a control system, and the main propulsion system), and a small lunar lander (called the lunar excursion module, or LEM, which also bore the more formal name lunar module, or LM)—would be boosted into Earth orbit on top of a three-stage rocket. Once in Earth orbit, the third stage of the rocket would then propel the craft's three-person crew into a lunar trajectory. Reaching lunar orbit, two of the crew members would don space suits, climb into the LEM, detach it from the mother ship, and maneuver down to the lunar surface. The third crew member would remain in the command module, maintaining orbital vigil.

If all went well, after lunar exploration was concluded, the top half of the LEM would rocket back up to dock with the command module. After disembarking from the craft, astronauts would then separate the lander's top half from the command module. The LEM would subsequently be cast adrift into deep space or deliberately crashed into the lunar surface to measure seismic disturbances. The three astronauts, safe and secure in the command module, would head for home.

LOR eventually prevailed over the direct ascent and EOR methods, mainly because of the efforts of a group of Langley researchers. In the opinion of many historians, LOR was why the United States, in less than a decade, was able to manage humankind's first extra-terrestrial excursion.

A rough approximation of spacecraft rendezvous in lunar orbit had been formulated as early as 1923 by German rocket pioneer Hermann Oberth. In 1959, Langley researcher William H. Michael, Jr., wrote an unpublished paper that briefly sketched the benefits of "parking" the Earth-return propulsion portion of a spacecraft in lunar orbit on a Moon-landing mission. Two separate groups of Langley researchers—the Lunar Mission Steering Group and the Rendezvous Committee—began to examine Moon-mission mechanics in 1959 with Michael's work as a point of departure. Working at first independently, then together, the two groups became convinced that lunar-orbit rendezvous was NASA's best shot at lunar landing. NASA headquarters management, however, was not persuaded.

When Langley engineer and Rendezvous Committee head John C. Houbolt and a few of his colleagues initially approached NASA headquarters officials with the LOR idea, it was rejected as being unnecessarily complex and risky. Critics cited the danger: if the procedure should fail while the astronauts were orbiting the Moon, then they would be marooned forever in a metallic tomb. At least in the EOR scenario, if something went wrong, the astronauts could return home simply by allowing the orbit of their spacecraft to decay, reentering the atmosphere and then splashing down somewhere in an ocean.

Houbolt insisted and persisted, and after two years of sometimes heated discussions, NASA officials conceded his point: LOR was the way to go to the Moon. It would employ proven technology, incorporate a lighter payload, require only one Earth launch, and would use less total-mission fuel than either of the other two methods put forth. Moreover, and importantly, only the small and lightweight LEM would have to land on the Moon. Part of LOR's appeal was also design flexibility; NASA could independently tailor all of the Apollo modules to suit mission requirements. In July 1962 NASA administrator James Webb formally approved the LOR concept.

At a critical point in the early 1960s, Langley researchers were the only ones in NASA fighting for LOR. It is difficult to say what the outcome might have been had the concept not been adopted. But the fact remains that, in less than a decade after President Kennedy's to-the-Moon directive, American astronauts were strolling on the lunar surface.

There was a great deal of preparation for NASA's inaugural Moon shot. The Mercury program was the start. Astronaut Alan Shepard was the first American into space, although briefly; his suborbital mission lasted 15 minutes. John Glenn was the first American to orbit Earth, in February 1962, elating an American public eager for in-space success. After Mercury came Gemini, the project that would put to the test the maneuvers that would be required if Apollo was to be successful.

In particular, the Gemini astronauts would have to practice the rendezvous and docking techniques necessary to link two spacecraft. Accordingly, Langley built the Rendezvous Docking Simulator in 1963. Full-scale modules of the *Gemini* and *Apollo* spacecraft hung

Neil Armstrong, the first human to step on the surface of the Moon, at the Langley Lunar Landing Research Facility.

NASA Langley photo no. EL-1996-00223

1962 version of the Lunar Landing Simulator (inset).

The simulated lunar surface as seen from atop the Lunar Landing Research Facility.

NASA Langley Photo Nos. EL-2001-00396 (inset) and EL-2001-00401

from an overhead carriage and cable-suspended gimbal system, the whole assembly being attached to the rafters of the Langley Research Center West Area Hangar. Astronauts "flew" the vehicles to rehearse and perfect docking skills.

Because the Moon is airless and its gravitational field is only one-sixth the strength of Earth's, there are no direct parallels between atmospheric flying and the piloting of a lunar lander. Some distinctly unusual problems would have to be overcome for the first manned lunar landing. For example, the firing of rockets in vacuum in order to hover above the lunar surface could not be precisely duplicated by a similar maneuver in Earth's atmosphere. Also, the thrust of control rockets could produce abrupt up-and-down, side-to-side, or rolling motions. The light would be different, too; the harsh glare of sunlight on the Moon's surface was unsoftened by passage through an atmosphere, thereby throwing off depth perception.

To address these and other practical Moon matters, Langley built the Lunar Landing Research Facility (LLRF) in 1965. Twenty-four astronauts—including Neil Armstrong, the first human to walk on the Moon—practiced landings at this facility. Overhead cables supported five-sixths of the weight of a full-size model LEM, and thrust was provided by a working rocket engine. The LLRF base was modeled with fill dirt to resemble the Moon's surface and dark shadows were painted around the "craters." Floodlights were erected at the proper angle to simulate lunar light. A black screen was even installed at the far end of the gantry to mimic the lunar "sky." Neil Armstrong later said that

when he saw his shadow fall upon the lunar dust, the sight was the same as he recalled while training at the LLRF at Langley. Attached to an overhead, light-weight trolley track that was part of the LLRF was the Reduced Gravity Simulator. There, suspended on one side by a network of slings and cables, an astronaut's ability to walk, run, and perform the various tasks required during lunar exploration activities was evaluated.

The Center built other equipment to imitate lunar conditions. A simulator constructed at Langley in the early 1960s helped researchers determine the ability of a pilot to control vertical braking maneuvers for landings, starting from an altitude of about 25 miles above the lunar surface. There was also a special facility that improved one-sixth-scale models of the lander to gauge the impact of landing loads. Another laboratory apparatus probed the anticipated and much feared problem of blowing dust caused by rocket blast, which could obscure the lunar surface and prevent the LEM pilot from locating a safe landing spot. In addition, the Dynamics Research Lab was built to construct and test models of space vehicle systems, including a one-tenth scale model of the Saturn V rocket. Other studies there involved the analysis of fuel-sloshing dynamics in differently shaped tanks, including cylinders, ellipsoids, and toroids.

In 1959, specialists in the Dynamic Loads Division, who had researched problems in helicopter dynamics for 10 years, redirected their expertise to support the space program. The Dynamics Research Laboratory was designed, funded, and constructed as a fiscal year 1961 budget item. Plans were made to

A preparatory examination of a Lunar Orbiter.

NASA Langley photo no. EL-2001-00398

Lunar Orbiter 2 took this photo of an area of the Moon the size of Massachusetts, Connecticut, and Rhode Island.

NASA Langley photo no. EL-2001-00371

The floor of the crater Copernicus, which dominates the upper left quadrant of the Moon as viewed from Earth, photo taken by *Lunar Orbiter 2.*

NASA Langley photo no. EL-2001-00450

Earthrise photographed by the *Apollo 8* crew while in lunar orbit.

NASA Langley photo no. EL-2001-00365

construct and test numerous space vehicle systems including a one-tenth-scale model of the Saturn V rocket. Tests of this model were used to verify that the analytical models of the dynamics of the Saturn V vehicle were correct. As a result of this succesful program, Martin Marietta requested that similar dynamics tests be conducted of a one-fifth-scale model of the Titan rocket, supplied by them. Other studies involved the analysis and experimental test of fuel sloshing dynamics in numerous shapes of propellant tanks.

One of Langley's most noted achievements during this period was the design and management of the Lunar Orbiter project. Third in a series of NASA-sponsored programs designed to choose the most suitable landing spot for Moon-landing missions, Lunar Orbiter photographed nearly all of the lunar surface in a series of spectacular close-ups. Some of the lunarscapes of the far or "dark" side of the Moon had never before been seen by the human eye.

On April 16, 1964, NASA signed with prime contractor Boeing Corporation to construct Lunar Orbiter. Just 28 months later, on August 10, 1966, the first Orbiter blasted off on its ambitious trek. Eventually, five Lunar Orbiter spacecraft were launched. All five were successful. (The final launch occurred in August 1967.)

The craft essentially consisted of an 850-pound platform on which was mounted a built-to-order two-lens camera that took photos of the lunar surface on rolls of 70-mm aerial film. The film was actually developed on board the vehicle, pressed into contact with a web that contained a single-solution-processing chemical before it was read

The effects of wind and atmospheric turbulence on the Saturn rocket were studied in Langley wind tunnels.

NASA Langley photo no. EL-2001-00402

Then-CBS News anchor
Walter Cronkite tries out
the Langley Reduced
Gravity Simulator in 1968.

NASA Langley photo no. 68L08308

Alan Shepard with the
Lunar Excursion Module at
Langley. He was the first
U.S. astronaut in space and
fifth on the Moon.

NASA Langley photo no. EL-1996-00219

The Apollo Command and
Service Modules
photographed from the
Lunar Module while in
orbit around the Moon.

NASA Langley photo no. EL-2001-00483

out" and transmitted to Earth-based
receiving stations. Ninety-nine percent of
the Moon's surface was mapped by
Lunar Orbiter. Of the eight sites identified by *Lunar Orbiter 3* as appropriate,
one—in the Sea of Tranquillity—was
chosen as the place for the *Apollo 11*
landing.

At the time, Israel Taback was chief
engineer and spacecraft manager for the
program. He recalls an international conference in Prague, late in 1967, attended
by astronomers from all over the world
eager to see the photographic results of
the Orbiter project. Taback was equally
eager to oblige. Assisted by his wife,
Taback unrolled large photo sheets of the
lunar surface and covered them with
transparent plastic. Then, on a gymna-
sium floor in a renovated 16th century
school, and in their stocking feet, Taback
and his colleagues went for a stroll on the
Moon. "Sending off five spacecraft to
orbit the Moon," Taback observes, "and
then have them map the entire lunar surface... well, it was an astounding thing at
the time. And every one of them worked!
It was thrilling."

The Center space race efforts also
extended to wind tunnel and general
space-science research. Studied in
Langley facilities were the effects of buffeting by wind, structural integrity, heat
resistance, and the durability of instrument design. Systems engineering personnel worked with other NASA Centers
on cooling, heating, pressure, and waste-
disposal systems. "We were working
beyond the state of the art," says
Barton Geer, retired Langley director for
Systems Engineering and Operations.
"Nobody had done things like this
before."

Without Langley participation in the Mercury, Gemini, and Apollo programs, there likely would have been no American Moon landing by midsummer, 1969. As it was, on July 20 of that year, more than a billion people heard or watched Neil Armstrong take those first tentative steps upon another world. As he did so, Langley's entire staff could take justifiable pride in the indispensable role the Center played in a seminal event in human history.

"We had a target and a goal. Congress was behind it. Funding was available. The entire Nation mobilized for a common goal," says John Houbolt, retired chief aeronautical scientist. "The landing on the Moon was undoubtedly mankind's greatest technological and engineering accomplishment. We started essentially from scratch in 1962 and seven years later we were on the Moon. It was a remarkable achievement and remains unsurpassed."

Apollo's revelation to the earthbound was of a home planet of great beauty, a world that, compared with the barren inhospitality of the rest of the solar system, was a vivid reminder of the fragility of life. Seen from a distance, Earth appeared as a startling oasis of life, a bubble of animate color afloat in the ebony void of space. With astronauts

NASA Langley photo no. EL-2001-00427

On July 20, 1969, more than a billion people watched on television as Neil Armstrong took humankind's first steps on another world.

walking on the lunar surface and planetary probes opening human eyes to otherworldly landscapes, perspectives were beginning to change. A larger, more exciting, more wondrous universe beckoned. What other marvels awaited humankind as it audaciously roamed beyond the planet of its birth?

Space Shuttle scale model during
wind tunnel tests.

6

EXPERTISE APPLIED

In the aftermath of *Apollo 17*, the final lunar landing mission in 1972, it was sometimes hard to believe that a scant generation earlier interplanetary travel seemed the wildest fantasy. But even as humans took on the cosmos, there remained any number of vexing terrestrial problems. Those who lived during the 1960s will recall conflict of all sorts: political, social, cultural, and economic. The space program was not exempt from its share of controversy. Critics blasted Apollo as a flight of technological fancy that wasted precious dollars that otherwise could be spent bettering the lives of the disadvantaged. Supporters admitted that the space program was expensive but argued that the future payback, in terms of a deeper scientific understanding and improved technology, was enormous. The first part of that argument, of spinoff products from the space program benefiting the average citizen, was advanced more forcefully in coming years as NASA was thrust into the relentless media glare and asked to justify every action and explain every shortcoming.

As the Apollo program wound down, NASA seemed the victim of its very success. To use a sports analogy, the Super Bowl had been won: with the space race finished, there was no longer any space contest that needed winning. Some members of the legislative and executive branches of government felt that since NASA had done the job President Kennedy required of it, the agency could now finish whatever obscure research projects it wished—as long as it did not ask for a lot of money.

By the mid-1970s, the American public did not seem that interested in space. After the wrenching national pain of Vietnam, an embargo imposed by oil producers in the Middle East, and the arrival of "stagflation," it looked as though the United States might retreat from the space beachhead it had established. To be sure, there were impressive projects such as *Skylab*, a joint United States and Soviet Union rendezvous of the *Apollo 18* and *Soyuz 19* spacecraft, and the development of the Space Shuttle. However, few proposed any crewed program on the huge scale of the Mercury, Gemini, and Apollo programs.

At Langley, there was a period of belt tightening, staff cuts, and reduced budgets. In 1966, the Center employed some 4,300 civil servants, a figure that decreased by approximately 130 a year beginning in the early 1970s. By 1980 the staff work force numbered 2,900. Smaller, more focused programs with short term objectives were emphasized.

The role of contractors, made important during the Apollo years, increased. With less money to manage, Langley would have to establish priorities and decide how to balance the demands of aeronautical research with those of space science.

Characteristic of the more back-to-basics approach was an aeronautics program that began in 1972, when Langley joined with industry, university, and U.S. Air Force representatives in a study of ways to incorporate composite materials into new aircraft design. With the 1973–74 energy crisis, this effort was redirected and renamed. The resultant Aircraft Energy Efficiency (ACEE) program sought to identify any and all ways to use airplane fuel more efficiently. The broad aim was to provide an inventory of then-available and future technologies that could be used by aircraft manufacturers. The ACEE research was more specific and

Full-scale model of the HL-10 Lifting Body mounted in the Full-Scale Tunnel in 1964.

NASA Langley photo no. EL-2000-00438

concentrated in the areas of materials, structures, and aerodynamics.

The U.S. crewed space program was given a post-Apollo boost by development of the first Space Shuttle, models and prototypes of which underwent extensive testing in the late 1970s. With a long history of winged-vehicle experimentation including research on lifting bodies in the 1950s and 1960s, Langley took on primary design and aerodynamic research duties as the project went forward. In particular, Langley researchers were responsible for a crucial Shuttle design decision.

It was initially thought desirable to equip the Shuttle with jet engines that would drop into position as the craft reentered Earth's atmosphere and maneuvered for landing. But Langley researchers argued in favor of a dead-stick landing, during which the Shuttle would glide, unpowered, to a runway touchdown. Center personnel pointed out that a dead-stick landing would be less

complex, would reduce weight, and would be safe besides. Researchers cited the experience of 300 pilots of Boeing jet transports, trained in dead-stick landings, all of whom validated the concept. Although there was initial opposition to the Langley effort, NASA officials conceded the point as it became clear that the inclusion of jet engines would indeed increase the Shuttle's weight beyond acceptable limits. They were omitted from the final craft design.

Langley also initiated a major Shuttle support effort in its wind tunnels. There, Shuttle scale models spent more than 60,000 occupancy hours undergoing tests to verify aerodynamic soundness. Langley researchers conducted structures and materials tests, investigated and certified the thermal protection system of glued-on tiles, developed simulations to solve problems in the Orbiter's flight control and guidance systems, conducted landing tests on tires and brake systems, and later participated in the redesign of

Full-scale nonflying mock-up of HL-20 lifting body studied as a possible personnel launch system.

NASA Langley photo no. EL-2000-00565

Space Shuttle and booster configuration (left) in the National Transonic Facility at Langley in 1985.

A computational fluid dynamics (CFD) computer generated Space Shuttle model (right).

NASA Langley photo no. EL-2001-00411

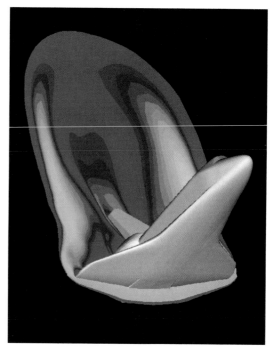

NASA Langley photo no. EL-2000-00567

Model of the Space Shuttle in the Langley 16-Foot Transonic Tunnel in 1978.

NASA Langley photo no. EL-1997-00091

solid-rocket booster components. Thus, when Space Shuttle *Columbia* soared to orbit on its April 12, 1981, maiden flight, Langley researchers could take considerable pride in the Center's contributions to the development of a new generation of spacecraft.

By the mid-1980s a new president, Ronald Reagan, had announced several aerospace initiatives, two of which— the building of a space station and the creation of the National Aero-Space Plane—would involve Langley Research Center directly. Reagan's successor, George H. W. Bush, had by 1990 outlined other ambitious plans, which included an increased American space-research presence in near-Earth orbit and a possible crewed mission to Mars by the end of the second decade of the 21st century. These, too, would call upon the research expertise of the Center.

In the last decade of the 20th century a new chapter in astronautics was being written. Faster, safer, more environmentally benign aircraft were on the drawing boards, and there were plans to make spaceflight more economical and thus attractive to private interests. A spirited debate had been joined over how best to use terrestrial resources while protecting Earth's biosphere; central to such discussions was how, for the first time in human history, to monitor and thereby understand planetary health. Aerospace technology of the sort pioneered at Langley seemed likely to be used not only as a means to better comprehend the workings of the home planet, but also to push beyond it, farther into space. While it did not seem likely that the year 2000 would usher the golden age predicted by some aerospace enthusiasts, there

appeared little prospect of technological retreat from 75 years' worth of amazing aeronautical advances.

MEETING MARS

In the 1870s and 1880s Italian astronomer Giovanni Virginio Schiaparelli identified features on the planet Mars that he believed to be an extensive system of canals. Schiaparelli and others theorized that Martians used the channels for irrigation, as aqueducts, or like the Italian island city of Venice, for transportation. In later years the Martian "canals" were shown to be the result of poor stargazing equipment and fanciful imaginations.

The question still persisted. Is there life of any kind on Mars? That was the primary question the Langley-led Project Viking hoped to answer. Begun in the late 1960s, and the largest space-science undertaking at the Center since the crewed space efforts, Project Viking's goal was a soft landing on the surface of Mars followed by limited exploration.

The ambitious project would confront engineering challenges not faced even by the complex Apollo program. Project Viking would entail the development of two vehicles that would travel on one spacecraft. Once at Mars, and while both vehicles were still connected, the Viking Orbiter would select a landing site for the Viking Lander, conduct scientific investigations using the Orbiter's onboard radio system, and study the planet's topography and its atmosphere. The Lander's work was more demanding. Essentially a lightweight, rugged, automated extraterrestrial laboratory, it had to maneuver to a soft landing on the

Viking I under assembly in clean room.

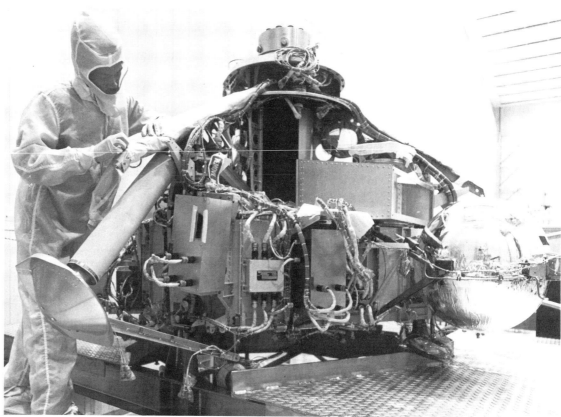

NASA Headquarters photo no. 74-H-325

Martian surface and then undertake a series of studies on Martian geography, weather, chemistry, and biology.

The Center asked for and received authorization to directly oversee the design and construction of the Viking Lander. In addition, Langley became the lead for Project Viking. Langley coordinated the entirety of the work undertaken by other cooperating NASA centers, such as the Jet Propulsion Laboratory in California, which was itself overseeing the design of the Viking Orbiter. Langley was also given responsibility for construction management of the two vehicles and their constituent instruments, which were built by private contractors.

Great technical sophistication was required to execute the scientific experiments, digitize the collected information, store the data, manipulate it, and then transmit it back to receiving stations on Earth. There was another crucial require-

ment as well. "One of the most critical things was the sterilization of everything on the spacecraft," says Langley researcher Eugene Schult, who came to Langley in 1949 and who retired as deputy chief of the Center's Terminal Configured Vehicle Office in 1980. "That included all electrical components, every part of the structure, all the fluids. We had to sterilize to insure that Mars would not be contaminated by any microbes imported from Earth."

All of this complexity and sophistication had a direct dollar equation: developing such an intricate machine in such a small package against a specific deadline required a large budget. However, NASA, and Langley, operated with a budget full of restrictions. Applying the lessons learned during the Mariner program, a Viking predecessor that sent a probe to Mars, demanded enormous

NASA Langley photo no. EL-1996-00220

Launch of the *Viking 2* on a Titan III Centaur rocket on September 9, 1975.

technical ingenuity and resourcefulness because of budget constraints.

In the minds of a few Langley dissidents Viking was more of a research curse than blessing. Some of those on the aeronautics side were especially resentful of the resources sucked up by the project. "There were a lot of people in the research lab who hated Viking," confirms Paul Holloway, Langley director from 1991 through 1997. "We were rebuilding aeronautics, taking on Viking, and being hit by a gigantic manpower reduction, all at the same time. Viking had priority over everything and dominated all of our space technology efforts. There was a major impact on our research. Computers were tied up; wind tunnel models could not get built. Yet even if it was one of Langley's most divisive projects, Viking was one of the Center's finest accomplishments."

Project Viking was not fated to answer all the questions posed by planetary scientists, but the fact that it addressed them was tribute to the engineering skill acquired at Langley after years of practice on such programs as Mercury, Lunar Orbiter, Gemini, and Apollo. On July 20, 1976, on the seventh anniversary of the first lunar landing and two weeks after the 200th birthday of the United States, *Viking Lander 1* touched down on the Martian surface. There, it and *Viking Lander 2*—which landed on September 3—transmitted back to Earth spectacular images of the bleak Martian landscape.

In mid-August of 1976, less than a month after *Viking Lander 1* touched down on the Red Planet, the craft's sampler arm extended a retractable boom and pushed over the rock that Langley researchers had nicknamed "Mr. Badger." Labeled thus because of its

The first photograph
taken by *Viking 1* on
July 23, 1976.

NASA Headquarters photo no. 76-H-624

Closeup of Martian
moon Phobos (left)
taken by *Viking Orbiter 1*
on February 20, 1977.

The planet Mars (right) as
seen from *Viking Orbiter 1*
on June 18, 1976.

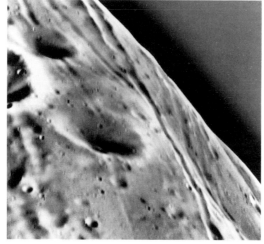

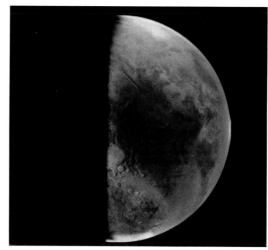

NASA Langley photo no. EL-2001-00411

NASA Langley photo no. EL-2000-00567

Rock called "Mr. Badger"
being lifted by Viking
collector arm (left) and
moved to left of original
position (right).

NASA photo no. PIA00528.6625

shape, Mr. Badger was one of four rocks named in honor of the book *The Wind In The Willows*. (Other rocks in the Willows Formation were given the titles Mr. Rat, Mr. Mole, and Mr. Toad.) Researchers were curious: would the soil under Mr. Badger be moister than the surrounding, exposed soil? If so, perhaps there would be evidence of organic chemical processes, processes that could indicate the presence of primitive life. Unhappily for those hoping to find definitive proof of extraterrestrial existence, the outcome was not conclusive.

Designed to function for 90 days, all four Viking craft exceeded manyfold their intended operational lifetimes. Orbiter 2 was the first to fail, on July 24, 1978. Lander 2 ceased operation on April 12, 1980, followed four months later by Orbiter 1 on August 7. Lander 1 stayed alive seven years past its design lifetime, until November 13, 1983, when it finally fell silent.

"To that day—maybe to this day—Viking was the most difficult unmanned space project ever undertaken. It brought Langley to the forefront of spacecraft technology," says Edgar M. Cortright, who arrived in Hampton in 1968 as Center director and who retired from that post in 1975. "One of the most emotional experiences is to be part of a team that knocks itself out doing something worthwhile, and then succeeding. When Viking landed it was a real high. There was a tremendous mixed sense of exhilaration—that we did it—and relief—that it did not fail. There was pride in the Langley team, pride in the accomplishment itself; it was the culmination of unbelievable effort. History was being made."

NASA Langley photo no. EL-2001-00438

Boulder-strewn field on Mars' Utopian Plain viewed from *Viking Lander 2* camera.

NASA Langley photo no. LV-00140

The first evidence of Martian frost, the white patches around the rocks, photographed by *Viking Lander 2.*

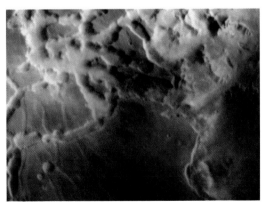

NASA Langley photo no. EL-2001-00437

Clouds of water ice (white patches) are visible in this view of a Martian sunrise taken by *Viking Orbiter 1.*

REVOLUTIONIZING INFORMATION EXCHANGE

Remembering that there was a time when American society did not enjoy a widespread dependence on computers has grown difficult for a generation that relies on computational machines for the most ordinary of tasks, from banking to bill paying. Few realize that the idea of computing machines was introduced as early as the 17th century and that working models were on the drawing boards during the 19th century. For a number of reasons, it was not until the 1930s that the first practical computers were introduced. Another 40 or so years would pass before room-filling, power-hungry early models gave way to smaller, more compact designs. By 1974 with the introduction of the personal computer, there began a momentum to miniaturization that today seems unstoppable.

For researchers engaged in scientific inquiry, the advent of the computer has been a godsend, revolutionizing the way information is transmitted, stored, and used, enabling the rapid, cross-connected flow of information so crucial to technological advance. Scientific exchange has accelerated to light speed, as researchers use workstations, desktops, laptops, telephones, modems, video equipment, and fax machines in a constant quest to remain connected and in touch. More recently, by the mid-1990s, the growth and subsequent explosive maturation of the Internet and the World Wide Web democratized knowledge exchange, reducing to seconds the time it takes to share information. What all of this may mean, in the long view of history, remains to be seen. At present, in the field of aerospace, the impact has been great.

At Langley, computers have forever changed the way that aerospace scientists and engineers do research. Langley researchers have used successive generations of ever more capable supercomputers to create models of airflow around assorted aerodynamic shapes flying at varying speeds and to gauge an aircraft's structural response to differing flight regimes. These studies in computational fluid dynamics (CFD) aim at predicting what will happen to a proposed aircraft design under real-world flight conditions. By evaluating variables long before a model is mounted in a wind tunnel test section, computers dramatically accelerate the entire design-and-test process. "The whole design can be looked at to see how one change in one area affects all the others," says Frank Allario, a former Langley director for Electronics. "In the past an aerodynamicist designed a particular shape. Then the structures people came in and built a structure around it. Then the controls people came in and fitted their instruments. Now the idea is to tackle the whole thing together, up front."

One of the biggest advantages afforded by computers is the real-time acquisition of data. At Langley's beginning, the engineers with the sharpest eyes would peer through tunnel observation ports, read the balance scales, and call out their readings to the individual acting as the recorder. It would be days, sometimes weeks, before the data were processed and the test results known. Using a computer that can also be programmed to vary tunnel conditions, such as Mach number, air temperature, and pressure, ensures researchers are provided with

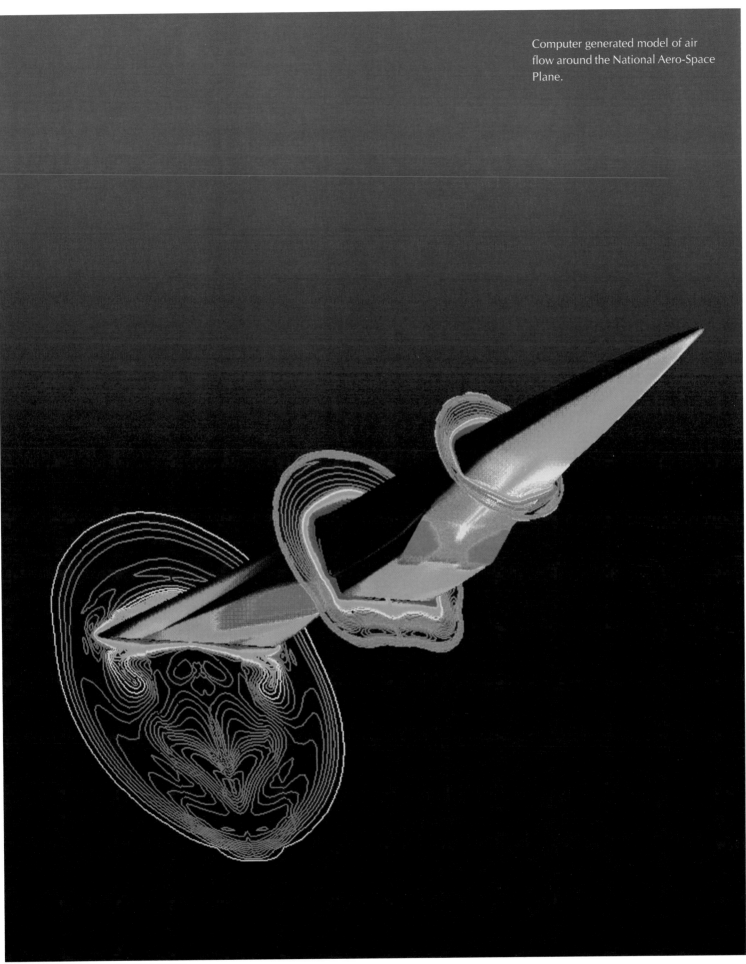

Computer generated model of air flow around the National Aero-Space Plane.

NASA Langley photo no. EL-2001-00433

up-to-the-second results of their investigations, thereby permitting ongoing adjustments to studies in progress.

At Langley, computers are also used to control the Center's simulators, which vary from full-motion devices to advanced versions of air traffic control systems. Langley's computer-controlled flight simulators create uncannily realistic in-flight conditions for pilots training on advanced fighter aircraft or for researchers testing modifications to flight systems, both under controlled laboratory conditions and at much lower costs than actual flight testing.

Digital avionics are among the most ambitious aeronautical applications of computer power. Whether as part of flight control systems, navigation and guidance systems, or employed to better orchestrate takeoffs and landings, digital avionics are changing the way aircraft

fly. Small television-like screens are a primary advantage enjoyed on avionics-equipped aircraft. A wealth of easy-to-read information on flight conditions can be displayed for quick evaluation by pilots. "On-board computers can take real-time data and actually tell a pilot what can or should be done, especially if something goes wrong," says Jeremiah F. Creedon, Langley Center Director from 1997 through June 2002, and now Associate Administrator for the NASA Office of Aerospace Technology in Washington, D.C. The rapid evolution of digital avionics is making for safer, easier-to-operate, and in the case of military craft, more maneuverable aircraft. From the early 1970s through the present, Langley has initiated or participated in a number of programs designed to evaluate these promising systems and their appropriate roles in military and commercial aviation.

Former Center Director Dr. Jeremiah F. Creedon (left).

A research flight deck simulator (right).

Langley Office of External Affairs photo archives

NASA Langley photo no. EL-1998-00039

STRONG LIGHTWEIGHT MATERIALS

Beginning in the 1960s and continuing through the present, the Center has worked to develop new composite materials, already supplementing and perhaps even eventually replacing metals and metallic alloys. One composite is composed of small rod-like fibers embedded in a binding substance, or matrix (similar to the way steel rods reinforce concrete). The material has demonstrated a considerable improvement in performance over typical aircraft materials. Many aircraft flying today have composite parts. Center researchers are seeking ways of employing composites in other aircraft structures and are working with aircraft manufacturers to identify the best means to do so.

"In 1970 there was no—not one—college course on composite materials at any university in the country," says Charles Blankenship, formerly the Center's director for Structures. "Langley was the lead in getting these courses at universities. We've had to educate our engineers in a whole new field, in a new technology. And it's been quite an education over the last few decades.

"We've built a lot of things out of metal. We've come to know metal and its properties quite well. What composites offer us is more than one choice. Designers will have a lot of flexibility: They'll be able to use aluminum where it makes sense and composites where they make sense. There will be more options."

One of the most attractive features of composite materials is their weight-saving potential. Contemporary graphite-epoxy composites available from com-

NASA Langley photo no. EL-2000-000018

mercial sources demonstrate strength and stiffness as high as steel but at one-fourth the weight. Applied to full-body aircraft—wings, fuselage, and control surfaces—the structural weight reduction can be as much as 25 percent, which would generate enormous savings in fuel costs alone. According to a NASA-commissioned study done in 1991, if current composite-materials technology would then have been applied to the entire commercial U.S. aircraft fleet, the annual benefit would have amounted to some $2 billion.

Composites are quite resistant to structural fatigue—a small crack in a graphite-epoxy composite spreads much more slowly than one in aluminum, for example—and because they are nonmetallic, composites do not rust. The materials also have another major advantage: an ability to be precast into much larger, blended-body shapes, an example of which is a single part comprising wings joined to fuselage. This translates into a need for fewer fasteners and joiners, reducing parts cost and, in theory,

LaRC Macro Fiber Composite actuator for buffeting alleviation for 1/6 scale F/A-18 model.

A corrugated shell made from graphite rods embedded in an epoxy matrix.

NASA Langley photo no. EL-2001-00404

A full-scale segment of a graphite-composite wing undergoing tests in the Langley Structures and Materials Research Facility.

NASA Langley photo no. EL-1996-00139

permitting designers to routinely mass-produce at moderate price what today would be called custom-made airplanes. The use of composites is not yet widespread, at least in airplane manufacture. The price of the materials remains high, in large part because of labor-intensive manufacturing methods. Much also remains to be learned about the materials' durability over time and under adverse conditions. Langley is among those in the public and private sector looking for ways to reduce composite-materials costs while validating real-world performance.

Ultimately, future generations of aircraft may incorporate intelligent machine systems technology, also know as IMS. Such systems—computer-directed, built from composite materials and outfitted with sensors connected by fiber-optic "nerves"—would mimic the human body's own network of nerves and sense organs. Like humans, "smart" systems would be able to respond and adapt to a changing environment, to extremes of temperature and pressure, for example. One day, IMS-equipped devices may even be capable of limited self-repair. If such systems are ever built on a large scale—and Langley is testing small-scale IMS devices—then airplanes and spacecraft would undergo yet another remarkable design revolution.

Science In Space

Although both the United States and the former Soviet Union have been orbiting either machines or people about Earth since the late 1950s, there remains much to learn about the unique environment of space. How do materials and coatings react to near-constant bombardment by solar radiation or collision with

NASA Langley photo no. EL-2001-00468

Tomato seeds are prepared for launch in the Long Duration Exposure Facility.

NASA Langley photo no. EL-1994-00474

The Long Duration Exposure Facility being deployed by the Space Shuttle *Challenger* on April 7, 1984.

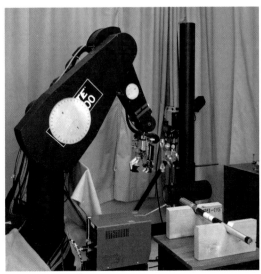

NASA Langley photo no. EL-2001-00413

Evaluating assembly of structures by robots.

The Langley-designed ACCESS helped determine the feasibility of in-space construction.

NASA Johnson photo no. 61B-41-019

extraterrestrial debris, like micrometeoroids? Do living systems fare well or poorly in almost total weightlessness? What are the effects of temperature extremes on organisms and structures?

Langley Research Center designed and built the Long Duration Exposure Facility, LDEF, to begin answering such questions. Completed by 1978, tested for structural soundness in 1979, LDEF was shipped to the Kennedy Space Center in Florida in mid-1983 for a 1984 deployment by the Space Shuttle *Challenger*. The bus-size LDEF structure was outfitted with 57 experiments developed by more than 200 researchers, both in the United States and abroad. The investigators represented universities, private industry, and government laboratories, including Langley and other NASA centers. Experiments fell into four broad categories: materials and structures, power and propulsion, science, and electronics and optics. LDEF was planned to orbit Earth for ten months as a passive satellite; those experiments needing power received it internally from already affixed batteries or solar cells. No telemetry was transmitted to or received from the craft.

The explosion of the Shuttle *Challenger* in 1986 extended LDEF's mission life to nearly six years as NASA reorganized Shuttle mission manifests in the aftermath of the tragedy. When LDEF was retrieved in January 1990 by the Shuttle *Columbia*, the vehicle was seen as a virtual treasure trove by investigators eager to know how its cargo had weathered an inadvertently long orbital sojourn. A preliminary finding revealed that space structures made from composite materials need a coating to protect

them from micrometeoroids, space debris, and degradation. Once on Earth, another LDEF experiment also bore fruit, so to speak: individuals and students worldwide were able to produce normal tomatoes from tomato seeds exposed to cosmic and solar radiation.

At the end of November 1985, an important Langley engineering experiment was put through its paces courtesy of the crew of the Space Shuttle *Atlantis*. Space-suited astronauts, working from *Atlantis'* cargo bay, snapped together a 45-foot-long ACCESS (Assembly Concept for Construction of Erectable Space Structure) truss tower. The structure, which consisted primarily of tubular aluminum struts connected by joint-like nodes, was designed by Langley researchers and constructed by Center technicians. The purpose of the exercise was to determine the feasibility of future in-space construction techniques and materials. The ACCESS experiment, concluded in about an hour, went smoothly and validated the practicality of in-space construction The experience later would prove invaluable during on-orbit construction of the International Space Station.

At Langley, a variety of investigations aim to identify the best way to design, build, and deploy large space structures, both manned and robotic. Other constructs, like huge communications antennas, may be deployed to channel ever-increasing amounts of data and information to distant points on the globe. Center researchers are developing automated systems that one day may assist human controllers in creating such apparatuses.

UNDERSTANDING THE ATMOSPHERE

Even as efforts continued in space, in the 1980s scientists were only beginning to understand Earth's atmosphere and the complicated processes that maintain, renew, and change it. Langley's atmospheric sciences researchers are among those attempting to better comprehend the fundamental workings of the life-giving ocean of air that girds the planet. Formally organized in the 1970s, by the 1980s the Atmospheric Sciences Competency (ASC)—as the former Atmospheric Sciences Division was renamed in the late 1990s—had begun to examine the effect of clouds and cloud formation on global climate, the nature and extent of upper atmosphere ozone depletion, the dispersion patterns and effects of trace gases (those that influ-

ence the greenhouse effect), the atmospheric impact of large-scale burning of wood and vegetation (known as biomass burning), and the processes of global atmospheric chemistry in Earth's lower atmosphere.

"We can take an idea, a glimmer in the mind," says Don Lawrence, former Atmospheric Sciences chief, "take it all the way through to building a device, flying or orbiting that device, and processing and then analyzing the data that results. At Langley we've built, I think it's fair to say, a world-class atmospheric sciences program."

Langley's atmospheric investigators have designed a wide array of sophisticated instrumentation, including customized combinations of lasers, telescopes, and sensors that are flown on aircraft to measure extremely small concentrations

The Earth Radiation Budget Experiment (ERBE) satellite prior to launch.

NASA Langley photo no. EL-2001-00409

of gases, small particles, and water vapor. ASC scientists have fashioned satellite-based devices that gauge heat energy, have designed helicopter-borne instruments that analyze gaseous and solid emissions from fires, and are working on advanced sensing packages that will be orbited on future generations of satellites. ASC researchers have also devised software programs to analyze the enormous amount of data generated from ongoing global atmospheric experiments.

One principal ASC endeavor has been the design and management of the Earth Radiation Budget Experiment (ERBE), conceived to measure and analyze fluctuations in the amount of heat energy emitted by the Sun and reflected or absorbed by Earth. Determining the whys and wherefores of Earth's thermal equilibrium enables investigators to better understand the factors that drive world weather patterns and influence large-scale climate shifts.

The ERBE project was instituted in 1979, when Langley scientists first began to outline the program's scientific objectives and devise the requirements for the instrumentation to accomplish them. From the outset, Langley scientists managed the efforts of an international team of ERBE scientists and researchers, a team that is now some 60 members strong. One pivotal find was that clouds have a net cooling effect on global temperatures. "It really was a major scientific breakthrough," Lawrence says. "Now when climate modelers take clouds into account, they have quantifiable data to plug into their predictions."

Langley's atmospheric scientists in the 1990s also examined how humans have modified the atmosphere that

Artist's concept of Upper Atmosphere Research Satellite in orbit.

NASA Johnson photo no. S91-40833

Atmospheric Sciences at Langley are seeking to understand how we interact with our planet.

NASA Langley photo no. EL-1996-00155

Satellite image showing Pacific Ocean temperatures during El Niño/La Niña study.

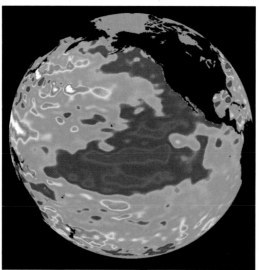

NASA Jet Propulsion photo no. PIA01528

Stratospheric Aerosol Gastropheric Experiment (SAGE)/Meteor-3M flight instrument in clean room prior to flight.

NASA Langley photo no. EL-1999-00043

surrounds and nurtures life on Earth. Will human destruction of vegetation and trees by burning have catastrophic consequences for this and succeeding generations? To answer such questions, teams of Center researchers have traveled all over the world to investigate the types and amounts of gases produced by human-induced burning of grass, vegetation, and trees. The emissions produced by such biomass burning are thought to add large amounts of carbon dioxide and other gases to the atmosphere.

Stratospheric ozone depletion has captured headlines, piqued the curiosity of average citizens, and generated intense scientific effort. In 1985, a team of international scientists confirmed the existence of an ozone hole in a large region directly over the continent of Antarctica. Additional experiments have shown that ozone depletion is also occurring over the North Pole. Langley researchers have worked with colleagues all over the world to assist in plotting ozone-hole fluctuations. Indeed, a Langley study was the first to explain the mechanism by which ozone depletion is intensified.

Another Langley Atmospheric Sciences-directed project is the Halogen Occultation Experiment (HALOE), launched in mid-September 1991 on the NASA Upper Atmosphere Research Satellite (UARS). The UARS instruments are intended to measure concentrations of ozone, methane, water vapor, carbon dioxide, carbon monoxide, hydrogen fluoride, and several types of chlorofluorocarbons (CFCs). HALOE is one of 10 separate instrument packages designed to provide atmospheric scientists with integrated global measurements of the chemistry, dynamics, and energy flows throughout various regions of the atmosphere. Other projects, like the Sounding of the Atmosphere using Broadband Emission Radiometry project, or SABER, and the Stratospheric Aerosol and Gas Experiment, or SAGE, are enhancing scientists' understanding of the fundamental processes governing chemistry and dynamics at middle and upper levels of the atmosphere.

Practical spinoffs from basic scientific research, such as improved instrumentation, faster computers, and a maturing space industry, are fueling further research into the complicated functioning of the atmosphere and its interaction with Earth's vast oceans. Studies such as those conducted by and with Langley aim to identify, in unmistakably quantitative terms, the impact on the atmosphere of an ever-burgeoning human population. It is only through such studies that reliable information can be gathered, information that can be made available to citizens and policy-making boards for the regulatory decisions that will undoubtedly have to be made in the future.

TRANSFERRING TECHNOLOGY

When driving through heavy rain on interstate highways, few motorists today realize that their automobile travels have been made substantially safer by a research program undertaken at Langley Research Center. Begun in 1962, the Center's hydroplaning program (hydroplaning is the loss of traction on a water covered surface) was originally intended to increase airplane tire traction, thereby decreasing braking distance. Langley's investigations concluded that the best

way to help aircraft tires maintain firm contact on wet pavement was to cut thin grooves into that pavement. The grooves would allow excess water to be forced away by the tire pressure on the pavement, which results in more direct contact of the tire with the pavement and better control of the aircraft. After tests in the late 1960s and early 1970s validated the concept, safety grooving was adopted for use on hundreds of airport runways around the world.

The practice also seemed appropriate for highways. Every state in America has since grooved at least part of its highway system. Safety grooves also have been cut in pedestrian walkways, ramps, and steps; food processing plants; work areas in refineries and factories; swimming-pool decks; and playgrounds. In 1990, the advance was selected for inauguration into the Space Technology Hall of Fame in Boulder, Colorado.

"It seems mundane when you think of it," says Cornelius Driver, who arrived at Langley in 1951 and retired in 1986 as chief of the then Aeronautical Systems

NASA Langley photo no. EL-2001-00038

Safety grooving has made highway travel safer.

At the Langley Aircraft Landing Dynamics Facility, a jet of water propels a test carriage at aircraft landing speeds to measure stresses on aircraft landing gear and tires. Aircraft tire after tests is shown in the inset.

RUN 20 DATE DEC 5
SPEED 166
SINK RATE N.A
YAW ANGLE 2   T 2
RUNWAY KSC G 5

NASA Langley photo nos. 88L09867 and EL-2001-00470 (inset)

Division, "but grooving affects more people, and has saved more lives, than anything NASA has ever done. The amount of money put into [grooving research] was piddling, but the savings in human life and resources from highway grooving alone could probably pay for every one of the NASA budgets from day one. In the broadest sense, such an accomplishment shows that government-sponsored research can have a tremendous payoff."

When such programs as the one that resulted in safety grooving are described to Langley researchers as a "break-through," many are made uneasy by the word. They feel that it is too exaggerated a term to properly describe the Center's precise application of engineering science. The word "spinoff" is considered more appropriate in describing programs that result in innovative devices or procedures that have application in areas well beyond their original purview.

Take the case of the Center's "riblet" research. Building on marine-science studies into sharks' streamlined shapes, in the mid-1980s a Langley team found that V-shaped grooves a few thousandths of an inch deep reduced aerodynamic drag. That seemed promising enough, but the work caught the attention of yachtsman Dennis Conner, who was about to compete in the 1987 America's Cup. Conner eventually affixed to the hull of his craft *Stars & Stripes* a commercially produced, thin-plastic film grooved with thousands of riblets. In the words of the Australian skipper Ian Murray, whose yacht *Kookaburra III* Conner eventually defeated, the American thereby "found a tenth of a knot more than anyone else."

NASA Langley photo no. EL-2001-00453

Projections on a shark's skin, dermal denticles, magnified 30 times revealing grooves.

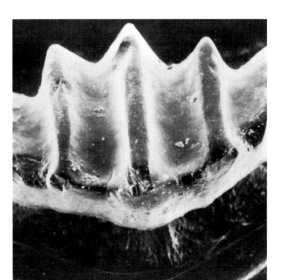

NASA Langley photo no. EL-2001-00426

A shark's dermal denticle magnified 3000 times.

NASA Langley photo no. EL-2001-00479

Manufactured riblets.

NASA's new two-in-one laser technology may eventually replace the dentist's drill for preparing fillings and the dentist's scalpel for gum surgery.

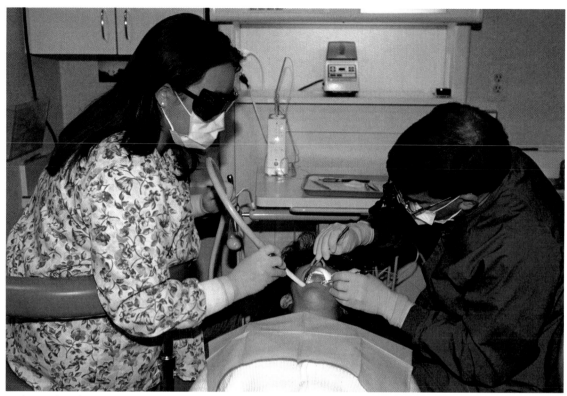

NASA Langley photo no. EL-2000-00138

There have been other Langley spinoffs as well. Project FIRE in the late 1950s and early 1960s led to the development of a furnace capable of melting metals for recycling. Nondestructive materials evaluation led to an ultrasonic device that uses sound waves to aid in the treatment of burn victims. Other notable examples of dozens of products that have been derived from work in Langley research facilities include a portable element analyzer that can detect such elements as gold, uranium, tungsten, and copper; a hand-held plastic welding gun suitable for use in space; a lightweight, composite-materials wheelchair for use on commercial airplanes; a polymer superplastic to protect space-borne materials from damage and radiation; a dental probe to assess gum diseases; a child-presence sensor that would notify parents if children were inadvertently left in car seats; and PETI-5, a high performance composite material that won the NASA Commercial Invention of the Year award

in 1998. PETI-5 can be used in parts and structures for reusable launch vehicles, subsonic commercial and military aircraft, missiles, space planes, electronic components, jet engines, and automobile engines.

By 1993, Langley had set up a formal commercialization effort. First known as the Technology Applications Group, the Technology Commercialization Program Office (TCPO) has responsibility for publicizing and marketing all of the Langley technology transfer efforts. The office's mission is to identify potential technology applications and create teams of nonaerospace customers and Langley technologists to expedite commercialization of Center inventions. In the process, TCPO also determines and protects the federal government's rights to patentable inventions made by NASA and contractor employees and provides legal counsel with respect to NASA's rights in intellectual property matters.

Picture from weather satellite data showing areas of nighttime illumination on Earth.

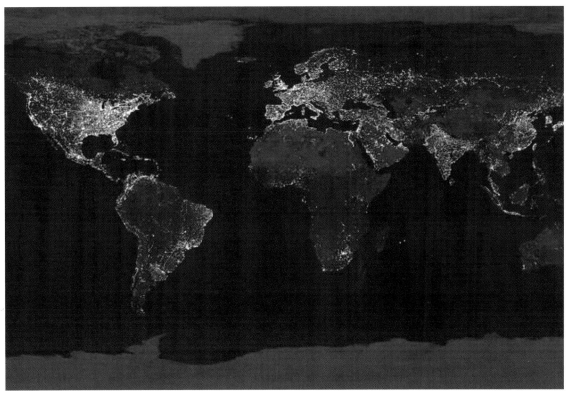

NASA Johnson photo no. PIA02991

In 1996, a Langley technology that might make everything from speakers to heart pumps smaller and more efficient was recognized as one of the year's 100 most significant technological advancements by *Research and Development Magazine*. Selected by a panel of distinguished scientists and engineers, the R&D 100 awards are presented annually by the magazine to the innovators of the 100 most technologically significant new products of the year from around the world. Langley's innovation, dubbed THUNDER for thin-layer composite-unimorph piezoelectric driver and sensor, may eventually find use in electronics, optics, irregular-motion suppression, noise cancellation, pumps, and valves. The material's low-voltage capabilities could allow it to be used within the human body in biomedical applications like heart pumps.[1]

THUNDER researchers at Langley took advantage of well-known phenomena exhibited by piezoelectric materials, which generate mechanical movement when subjected to an electric current or generate electrical charge in response to mechanical stress. Langley researchers created a piezoelectric material that was tougher, more durable, allowed lower-voltage operation, had greater mechanical load capacity, and could be easily produced at a relatively low cost, lending itself easily to mass production.[2]

The first generation of THUNDER devices is fabricated by building up layers of commercially available ceramic wafers and using a Langley-developed polymer adhesive. The process results in a prestressed device with significantly improved performance. The process is controllable and results in highly uniform pieces of hardware. Ideally, piezoelectric ceramic materials would be ground to a powder, processed, and blended with an adhesive before being pressed, molded, or extruded into wafer form. The result would be increased ability to tailor properties, more flexibility in choosing methods of manufacturing, and increased amenability toward mass production. THUNDER wafers could range in size from a few square millimeters to several square meters and thicknesses of fractional millimeters to several millimeters.[3]

In 1999, a thermoplastic hailed as a breakthrough in solar propulsion and power won the same recognition as had THUNDER. The thermoplastic was adapted for use on solar-powered satellites by SRS Technologies, Huntsville, Alabama, and should eventually be incorporated in aerospace and consumer products. When cast as large thin films, the thermoplastic material serves exceptionally well as solar-thermal concentrators for space-based propulsion and power concepts and, potentially, for inflatable large space antennas. Langley researchers developed the thermoplastic technology—actually, two similar polyimide chemical compounds—in a successful effort to improve the solar energy absorption and reflectance of existing space-based systems. Either compound can take the form of a highly transparent and nearly colorless thin film, with superior solar-energy characteristics such as resistance to the environmental extremes of space. The compounds are lightweight, simple, and economical for space-launch applications.[4]

Benefits to the end user can be dramatic. For example, SRS has developed fabrication processes to cast precise thin-film segments for use as power augmentation panels for a satellite manufacturer; these processes promise to increase the power production of the satellite's standard photovoltaic arrays. Future aerospace applications may include use

in optics for space telescopes or space-borne lasers; antennas for communications, surveillance and positioning; solar shielding; and aircraft and missile cabling. Commercially, the technology may be applied to many products, such as ultraviolet-resistant additives to paint and in components in flexible, printed circuit boards and liquid-crystal displays.[5]

In 2002, Langley researchers worked with Baby Beats, Inc. and Washington State University's Small Business Development Center—both based in Spokane—to transfer and develop aerospace technology originally created to better understand airflow over airplane wings into a portable, noninvasive, easy-to-use fetal heart monitor. "Because the material we used for wing-surface measurements is flexible, it's ideally suited to fit over the curved surface of a maternal abdomen for fetal testing," says Dr. Allan Zuckerwar of the Langley Advanced Measurement and Diagnostics Branch.[6]

The existing fetal heart-monitoring devices generally work well but cost many thousands of dollars, and the majority can only be used in a clinic or doctor's office. Langley developed the portable technology by responding to a request for assistance from Dr. Donald Baker, a physician whose practice includes remote areas where appropriate health care is difficult to obtain, and where there is increased risk of fetal mortality. An at-home patient can place the saucer-shaped monitor on her belly and tune a computerized control device to hear the fetal heartbeat. She then adjusts for the strongest signal, which can be transmitted directly to the doctor's office over phone lines. Baby Beats, Inc.,

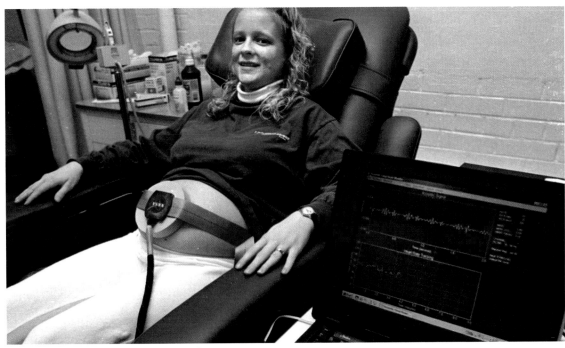

Langley Office of External Affairs photo archives

Dr. Baker's newly formed company, planned to begin manufacturing and marketing the monitor by the end of 2002.[7]

Baker's concern for tiny hearts began more than 25 years ago when he noticed the need for a portable heart rate monitor during obstetrics rounds in medical school. He watched as an unborn baby's heart rate, monitored by a fetal heart monitor strapped to the mother's belly, suddenly became dangerously irregular. A nurse hurried over and turned the pregnant woman on her side. The baby was inadvertently sitting on its own umbilical cord.[8]

Today, Baker envisions mothers with high-risk pregnancies and those who have trouble traveling to a doctor's office as the primary users of the monitor. He says his commitment heightened after working as a family doctor in the Flathead Indian Reservation in Montana early in his career. Baker, a member of the Minnesota Chippewa tribe, points out that pregnant mothers living in remote areas might be hours from a doctor's

office and may not have the financial resources to travel quickly or often. Inner-city mothers who have difficulty making it to a clinic could benefit from the monitor as well, as can most women with high-risk pregnancies. "Whether they are rich or poor, mothers love their babies," the Spokane physician says. "They want to take care of their baby but, when they are hours away from health care, it's very hard. This helps dignify health care and puts control in the parents' hands."[9]

For Langley, demonstrating the practical benefits of aerospace research would prove critical as the Center and NASA at large would once again come under economic and political scrutiny as planners dealt with unrelenting budget pressures. Different national priorities were emerging in the last decade of the 20th century. Establishing institutional priorities—how and why, and where, monies should be spent—would be the next step as Langley reexamined its research commitments and the role it would play within its parent agency.

The International Space Station
photographed during shuttle mission
STS-106.

NASA MSFC photo no. MSFC-0006654

7

REDEFINING ROLES

Just after World War II, German-born Wernher von Braun, brought to the United States to work on the space program after the Allied victory in World War II, foresaw rapid technological progress, particularly with space launch and exploration. Clearly, humans would reach assertively and rapidly into and beyond Earth orbit. It would only be a matter of decades before people would routinely live outside the earthly biosphere. Colonists would reach their homes through a combination of ingenuity, hard work, and, of course, brand new hardware that would make such sojourns routine.

A halfway point, a kind of orbital train station, was envisioned, wherein arriving and departing rocket flights would either deposit or pick up cargo and passengers. Historian James Hansen, in his book *Spaceflight Revolution*, quotes rocketeer von Braun as characterizing development of a space station in an article for the magazine *Colliers* as "inevitable as the rising sun." Once in space, humans, von Braun believed, would stay. Aiding in that sojourn would be an Earth-orbiting base, "an artificial moon from which a trip to the moon itself would be just a step." Carried in pieces, the station would be assembled by workers who would have an unparalleled view of the entire planet during their labors.

As the country's crewed space program developed and the decision was made to send astronauts to the Moon, lunar-orbit rendezvous trumped the competing concept of Earth-orbit rendezvous. There was no further need to build a space station as a jumping-off point for a Moon landing. Three decades would pass after von Braun's remarks before the United States committed to building the International Space Station. Langley's contributions to the Station included design and materials studies, as well as Center-developed structural components incorporated during on-orbit construction.

"To do the things in and out of NASA that NASA wanted NASA to do requires money. No bucks, no Buck Rogers, as they say in the movie *The Right Stuff*," says Tom Crouch, author of *Aiming for the Stars: The Dreamers and Doers of the Space Age* and senior curator of aeronautics for the Smithsonian Institution's Air and Space Museum. "What the space station became was a way to turn to another page. It was a minimum goal

NASA had to shoot for. Without it, you're not building toward the future of a human space program. You're simply sending up the Shuttle. But once the space station got going, the budget got out of hand."

In general in the 1990s, money was hard to come by for the agency. In the absence of a clearly defined geopolitical threat (abruptly redefined on September 11, 2001, by terrorist attacks on New York City and Washington, D.C.)—such as that thought to have been posed by the Soviet Union in the 1960s, or a clearly defined national goal such as a mission to Mars—NASA's budget was subject to conflicting forces, including pressure in the early to mid-1990s for all government agencies to substantially reduce costs.

A concept model for a space station in 1961.

NASA Langley photo no. EL-2000-00415

A report issued in February 1995 by the NASA Advisory Council Federal Laboratory Review Task Force starkly spelled out the challenge facing the agency. "NASA is currently undergoing dramatic and necessary change," asserted the report's authors. "The first factor is a major change in anticipated budget, [currently] $14.5 billion [and] increasing at the annual rate of 14 percent from fiscal year 1988 through fiscal year 1992. It is now projected to decrease to less than $11.5 billion in purchasing power by fiscal year 1999."[1]

There would be less "big" science and engineering and more focused commercial application.[2] Modest, but often ambitious in cost return, programs and projects like the missions to Mars, Earth-observing systems, and robotic flybys were a priority. All agency centers were expected to find ways of accomplishing their research missions more efficiently, even with relatively anemic budgets. Langley was no exception.

"It was no more the 'give us some money, we'll go off and do good things, and the world will be a better place as a result,'" says former Langley Center Director Creedon. "The research-for-its-own-sake paradigm was no more. You had to demonstrate that what you did, what you do, matters. We all knew that we were in for some belt-tightening."

For Langley, the 1990s proved both painful and rewarding. Forces larger than Langley affected its people, programs, and priorities. Money diminished, incentives were offered to reduce staff, projects were cut back or ended entirely, and the future seemed less certain than even after the *Apollo* years. Two employee buyouts and two large reorganizations occurred. According to Langley

NASA JPL photo no. PIA01120

Mars Pathfinder Lander at Ares Vallis on Mars in 1997.

Image of Jupiter's moon Io obtained by the Galileo spacecraft during a flyby.

NASA JPL photo no. PIA01667

figures, overall employment by 2002 dropped nearly 30 percent from the 1994 level of 6,000, down to 2,365 civil servants and 1,935 contractors. Several wind tunnels were closed, or in the case of the Full-Scale, or 30- by 60-Foot Tunnel, transferred to educational use in the form of a partnership with Old Dominion University in Norfolk, Virginia. It would be a time of cautious incrementalism, of managing changes in staffing and money while attempting to keep key programs intact.

"To my mind, the biggest single story [in the 1990s] is how the institution was grappling with the implications of the end of the Cold War. The public's interest in federal investment in aeronautical R[esearch] and D[evelopment] evaporated. It's gone," says Deborah Douglas, curator of science and technology for the Massachusetts Institute of Technology Museum in Cambridge, Massachusetts. Douglas was visiting historian at Langley from 1994 through 1999. "How do you go from one scientific paradigm to another? In aviation, the key paradigm was set up shortly after the Wright brothers made their first flight. That's what can be called 'normal' science. Over its his-

tory, Langley generally has not shaken the paradigm, but extended understanding in this normal-science realm, filling in big blocks of understanding."

Langley, Douglas believes, has unique research facilities that do not exist anywhere else in the world. But there are no calls for construction of any new wind tunnels or major refurbishment of existing facilities. In part that's because computers are assuming a greater role in aerodynamic modeling and forecasting. But it's also in part because NASA, under former Administrator Daniel Goldin, emphasized the third letter in the agency's title. That is, space-related research trumped aeronautics research, at least in terms of funding. "Bright people who used to work on aero[nautics] projects are now working on space," Douglas says. Even so, she believes Langley made gains in technology programs in the 1990s.

Such advances included development of sensors to detect and guard against clear-air turbulence, which can damage airplanes and injure passengers. Center engineers developed all-composite structures, which reduced an aircraft's weight while improving performance. Innovations were made in materials systems, aircraft controls, noise reduction, and computational analyses. Throughout, one theme would constantly reemerge: that of usefulness. If an approach could not be shown to have a short- or medium-term payoff, then a large investment in either dollars or personnel could not be justified.

"The Nation has been less willing to fund what can be described as undefined or unstructured research," says Delma Freeman, Jr., acting Langley Director.

Replica of the Wright Brothers' 1902 glider undergoing investigation by Old Dominion University students in the Langley Full-Scale Tunnel.

Langley Office of External Affairs photo archives

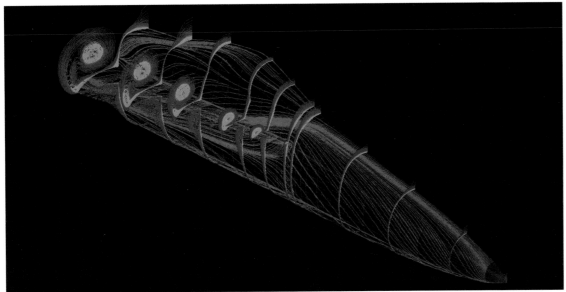

Computer-generated image of aerodynamic forces acting on a possible nose design for a fighter aircraft.

NASA Langley photo no. EL-2001-00430

By-pass ratio flow nozzle with noise suppression trailing edge in Langley Low Speed Aeroacoustic Wind Tunnel.

NASA Langley photo no. EL-1999-00444

F-16 model undergoing tests in the Langley Basic Aerodynamics Research Tunnel for the NASA High-Speed Research Program.

NASA Langley photo no. EL-1996-00201

"The path from idea to potential market-place position had to be clearer. We've moved into an era that requires a definite demonstration of a technology's usefulness. That's true in both aeronautics and space transportation."

Perhaps no one program would exemplify such realities more than high-speed research, whose greatest success would ironically be the cause of its demise. Begun just after World War II, high-speed research (HSR) focused on the ambitious technological goal of putting into the air faster-than-sound, environmentally friendly, economical jetliners that could shave hours of travel time between destinations in Asia and Europe. HSR was intended to serve two masters: technology and the economy. But a changeable global economy, the cost of advanced technology, the unexpected end-of-millennium explosive growth of the Internet, the rapid spread of cellular phone service, and the popularity of teleconferencing would combine to make rapid, long-distance travel seem less necessary.

HIGH-SPEED RESEARCH REDIRECTED

Langley's tradition of addressing the problems of flight with an eye toward their solutions seemed a natural fit for high-speed research. Logically, one could assume that if it was good to go fast between two widely separated spots, then it was better to go faster: supersonically, (650-plus miles per hour—Mach 1—or faster at cruising altitude), but affordably and at little or no harm to the environment. There were any number of technological innovations to devise, not to mention the economic imperative

NASA Langley photo no. EL-1999-00150

High-Speed Research technology concept airplane model in the Langley 16-Foot Transonic Dynamics Tunnel.

NASA Langley photo no. EL-1998-00162

A supersonic model in the Unitary Plan Wind Tunnel.

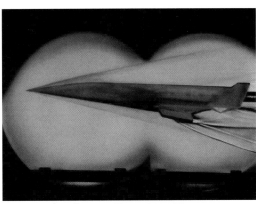

NASA Langley photo no. EL-2001-00415

A hypersonic aircraft undergoing tests in a wind tunnel.

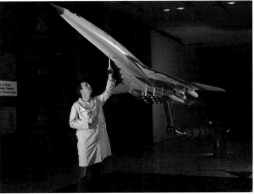

NASA Langley photo no. EL-1998-00235

Model of a high-speed civil transport concept in the Langley 14- by 22-Foot Tunnel.

of paying for it all with reasonable ticket prices and high passenger volumes.

Historian James Hansen is collecting information and conducting interviews for a six-volume documentary history of aerodynamics in America. Hansen says that what was then called the High-Speed Civil Transport program, or HSCT, was formally inaugurated in 1989 and looked to develop supersonic transport technology compatible with such environmental concerns as atmospheric impact and emission reduction, community noise, sonic boom, and radiation. By 1990 NASA had organized this endeavor into a two-phase technology program— dubbed, in general, HSR for high-speed research—in partnership with the U.S. aircraft industry (Boeing, McDonnell Douglas, General Electric, and Pratt and Whitney). Phase I was designed to develop technology concepts for environmental compatibility and was completed in 1995. Phase II then began to further

define HSR concepts and demonstrate their economic viability. But matters were already beginning to go awry, as Hansen elaborates:

Much of the store had already been lost. Since 1985 Boeing's share of the global commercial aircraft market fell from 90 percent to less than 50 percent, resulting in some serious financial difficulty for the American giant—even though Lockheed was by that time out of the market and McDonnell Douglas was ailing (and later merged into Boeing). At the same time, France's Airbus moved from zero percent control to about 50 percent control of the global market share. With these concerns in mind, what advocates of the HSCT lobbied the Congress to do in 1999, rather than keep cutting the federal R[esearch] & D[evelopment] budget for aeronautics R[esearch] & D[evelopment], was restore it to the level of 1989, which

NASA pilot Michael Wusk makes a "windowless" landing aboard a NASA 737 research aircraft.

NASA Langley photo no. EL-1996-00102

would require an increase of $500 million (or 8.5 percent).[3]

Despite significant progress, the HSCT program was essentially eliminated by May 1999 when former NASA Administrator Daniel Goldin announced a budget cut of $110 million, along with significantly reduced funding for other key research projects such as noise reduction and lower aircraft emissions. "What forced this decision was the growing cost of the International Space Station, to which the aeronautics funds were to be redirected," Hansen says. "In his announcement, Goldin said that another $500 million to $1 billion would be required to be found in future years to fund ISS, due chiefly to shortfalls in what the Russians were supposed to be contributing."

For those convinced that research to advance crucial new aeronautical concepts such as the HSCT was critical to enhancing the national security and economic interests of the United States, the lack of commitment to funding aeronautics was more than disappointing. Hansen points out that since 1989, federal aeronautics research and development spending had already fallen from $1.3 billion per year to $640 million per year. This spending reduction happened even though aeronautical products represented the second largest export category in the U.S. balance of trade—valued at $69 billion, second only to agricultural products. At the same time research and development money was falling at home, the governments of Great Britain, France, Japan, Taiwan, China, South Korea, and Indonesia were all investing more heavily in aeronautics and building strong partnerships with their private-sector aeronautics companies. Much of Japanese attention, in fact, was on the future of high-speed transport. Their government announced in early 1999 that

Researcher monitoring instruments on Langley Aries flight research aircraft.

Synthetic vision flight
systems during test.

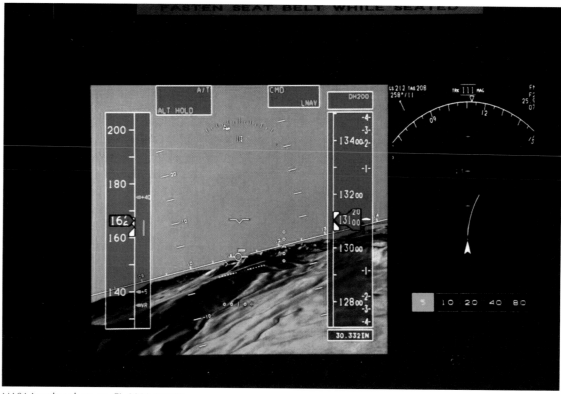

NASA Langley photo no. EL-2002-00059

$20 million was being spent as a first-year installment to establish a five-year program of supersonic transport research and development, the very activity that budget cuts were forcing NASA to abandon.[4]

"By the end of the century, the best aeronautic R[esearch] & D[evelopment] facilities in the world were again, as at the beginning of the century, in European countries," Hansen says. With an estimated $1 trillion global market for new and better airliners up for grabs between 2000 and 2010, many defenders of American aeronautics lamented that this was hardly the time to "give away the store."

For Langley, the HSR decision point was reached late in 1998, when Boeing opted out of high-speed research, citing promising but not mature technologies, high manufacturing costs, and lack of a viable market. Given that its primary

backer was withdrawing financial commitment, Langley felt it had no choice but to back out as well. "Industry was bringing a lot of money to the table," says Wallace Sawyer, former director of the Langley High-Speed Research Project Office. "When your primary industry partner steps back, you need to rethink at what rate and how much money to [invest in] commercial supersonic research. We cannot do things on our own."[5]

"The Center is doing all this research and it's tight with industry. And this huge focused program comes along," says Creedon, the former Langley Center Director. "The planning, tracking, and overhead increases. The money we're getting is also going up. Then, over two years, we lose 20 percent of our total funding, 30 percent of our research funding and 40 percent of funding for aerospace technology from NASA [Headquarters]. Cha-chung: The blade

Cockpit of research aircraft configured for synthetic vision flight test.

NASA Langley photo no. EL-2001-00068

fell. And the perils of an undiversified portfolio were visited upon the Center."

Despite cancellation by NASA Head-quarters, the HSR program did advance a number of technologies. Windowless or synthetic vision, for example, would later end up incorporated into all-weather, computer-aided views of aircraft systems, as well as fore, aft, and side visuals of conditions outside the cockpit. Computer design codes were devised that model aerodynamic loads and pressures, aiding in the design of commercial airplanes, space vehicles, and military craft. And engine redesigns, specifically to reduce ozone-damaging nitrogen oxides, but also to create quieter, more fuel-efficient engines, were also refined.[6]

One of the most robust technologies to emerge from the HSCT incubator was PETI-5, short for the fifth in a NASA-made series of composite materials known as phenylethynyl-terminate imide

formulations developed by Paul M. Hergenrother, Dr. John W. Connell, Dr. Brian J. Jensen, and Dr. Joseph G. Smith. Chosen as a NASA Commercial Invention of the Year in 1998, PETI-5 endured operational temperatures at 350°F for 15,000 hours, roughly equivalent to five years of continuous HSCT service. If the program had continued, plans called for PETI-5 to be certified for 60,000 hours, or approximately 20 years of regular flying. Nevertheless, the material is likely to see widespread use on future generations of aircraft and space vehicles, because of its light weight and ability to withstand high temperatures.[7]

AVIATION TECHNOLOGY MOVES TO INDUSTRY

High-speed research aside, Langley was also able to make significant contributions in the 1990s to subsonic flight, especially to a new Boeing jetliner,

Fiber reinforced composite materials.

NASA Langley photo no. EL-2001-00191

the 777. The Boeing 777 aircraft was designed for medium- to long-range passenger flights and is the largest twin-engine jet to be thus far manufactured, with first passenger-carrying flights conducted by United Airlines in May 1995. The Boeing 777 airframe incorporates durable lightweight composite aircraft structures, including graphite-epoxy floor beams, flaps, and tail assembly.

Software created by Langley experts was used in Boeing 777 product development, including fundamental mathematical procedures for airflow images, which enabled advanced computer-based aerodynamic analysis. The Center also conducted wind tunnel tests to evaluate flutter and vibration characteristics of the 777 aircraft's wing structure and to confirm the structural integrity of wing and airframe integration. In addition, Langley provided advice to Boeing on techniques for reduction of engine and

other noise for passengers and terminal area residents.

Radial tires like those used on the 777 underwent strength and durability testing at the Langley Aircraft Landing Dynamics Facility. Hampton researchers can also claim credit for advances that led to the aircraft's modern glass cockpit, a system that uses computer technology to integrate information and display it on monitors in easy-to-use formats; a digital data system, an easily reconfigurable computer network that allows aircraft computers to communicate with one another; a fly-by-wire system for control of wing and tail surfaces, replacing bulkier and heavier hydraulic control systems; and more frequent use of lightweight composite structures for increased fuel efficiency and range.[8]

"In the past decades we've moved well beyond the original Boeing 707. The 777 aircraft is an excellent example

Semispan model mounted in the National Transonic Facility at Langley.

NASA Langley photo no. EL-2000-00149

of that," says acting Center director Delma C. Freeman. "Within NASA the role Langley is uniquely qualified to play is that of atmospheric flight: all vehicles, all atmospheres. As long as the country is serious about aeronautics research, Langley will have the expertise to address a variety of issues across all speed regimes. One of the questions we have a tradition of asking is: what are the next generation of aircraft going to be?"

Part of that answer may lie with the Advanced General Aviation Transport Experiment (AGATE), a consortium of more than 70 members from industry, universities, the Federal Aviation Administration, and other government agencies. AGATE was created by NASA in 1994 to develop affordable new technology, as well as industry standards and certification method, for airframe, cockpit, flight training systems, and airspace infrastructure for single-pilot, next-generation, near-all-weather light airplanes. AGATE partners worked to make airplanes as easy to use as cars.

Along with a parallel program, General Aviation Propulsion, or GAP, which is geared toward development of revolutionary engines, AGATE provided industry with technologies that may lead to a Small Aircraft Transportation System (SATS) in the early 21st century. These investments support the national general aviation road map goal to "enable doorstep-to-destination travel at four times highway speeds to virtually all of the Nation's suburban, rural, and remote communities."[9]

The program has already led to a novel means of presenting critical flight path guidance information to the pilot. Dubbed "highway in the sky," the cockpit display system includes a computer-drawn aerial road map that the pilot follows to a preprogrammed destination. This highway is drawn on a highly intuitive, low-cost flat-panel display intended to displace decades-old "steam gauge" instrumentation. The system also includes a multifunction display of position navigation, a terrain map, and weather and air traffic information. In addition, digital radios will send and receive flight data, and a solid-state attitude and heading reference system will replace gyroscopes. Together, the displays and other equipment will provide enough information for a pilot to fly safely with reduced workload in nearly all weather conditions.[10]

In addition to transforming cockpits, the technology developed by the team is expected to redefine the relationship between pilots and air traffic control, fundamentally changing the way future general aviation pilots fly. This technology is expected to significantly increase freedom, safety, and ease-of-flying by providing pilots with affordable, direct access to information needed for future "free-flight" air traffic control systems. Pilots will have the ability to safely determine their routes, speeds, and proximity to dangerous weather, terrain, and other airplanes.

For the AGATE program, Langley engineers conducted crash tests evaluating structural integrity. A total of four airplanes were tested over a two-year period. The tests typically took place at about 60 miles per hour, into both packed-earth and hard surfaces, successfully demonstrating an improved shoulder harness system and energy-absorbing seats. The goal of the program was to

NASA Langley photo no. EL-2001-00463

Full-scale general aviation
aircraft undergoing
crashworthiness tests.

NASA Langley photo no. EL-2001-00464

NASA Langley photo no. EL-2001-00465

NASA Langley photo no. EL-2001-00466

Synthetic vision systems in flight tests.

NASA Langley photo no. EL-2002-00058

apply the techniques that have been successfully applied in military helicopters, race cars, and modern automobiles to improve survivability in crashes of small composite airplanes. A further goal was to reduce injury severity in survivable crashes. The program used a combination of analysis, subscale quasi-static testing, and full-scale crash testing to achieve these goals. In the final crash test, all of the crash dummies on board "survived" the crash, a first for general aviation crash tests.[11]

"In creating the AGATE, GAP, and SATS programs, NASA not only supported the technological revitalization of the U.S. general aviation industry, but Langley also incubated new ways of doing business through public-private partnerships," says Dr. Bruce J. Holmes, manager of the NASA General Aviation Programs Office. "Our theory was that the role of government should be to raise the tide of technology readiness across the entire general aviation industrial sector; the application of that theory estab-

lished the partnerships that collectively produced the most significant advancements in aviation technologies in the history of this industrial sector. The outcome of these Langley-led investments has been to lay the industrial, regulatory, and research foundations for the possibility that in the 21st century, smaller aircraft and smaller airports will play a vital role in public transportation."

In May 2002, NASA announced it had selected a partner for a joint venture to develop and demonstrate air-mobility technologies for transportation using small aircraft and small airports. A Langley neighbor, the National Consortium for Aviation Mobility (NCAM), also based in Hampton, will lead a public and private consortium of more than 130 members, working with NASA toward a mid-2005 proof-of-concept flight demonstration of new operational capabilities for technologically advanced small aircraft and small airports. One of NCAM's early tasks will be to coordinate the technology development of consortium members with NASA research. In a cost-sharing partnership between the federal government and the consortium, NASA and other federal agencies are expected to contribute up to $40 million to support the joint-sponsored research agreement.[12]

AN EMPHASIS ON SAFETY

Safety remained a major preoccupation of Langley aeronautics research in the 1990s. In response to a report from the White House Commission on Aviation Safety and Security, in 1997 Langley began leading NASA aviation safety research. The $500 million NASA Aviation Safety Program (AvSP) is a partnership with the Federal Aviation Administration, the Department of Defense, and the aviation industry. AvSP is working to develop advanced, affordable technologies to help make travel safer on commercial airliners and smaller aircraft. To meet the NASA goal of reducing the fatal aircraft accident rate by 80 percent in 10 years and 90 percent in 25 years, the safety program is focusing on three areas recommended by a national team of more than 100 government and industry organizations: accident prevention, accident mitigation, and aviation system monitoring and modeling.[13]

The safety program emphasizes not only accident reduction, but also a decrease in injuries when accidents do occur. The program includes research to reduce human-error-caused accidents and incidents, predict and prevent mechanical and software malfunctions, and eliminate accidents involving hazardous weather and controlled flight into terrain. The program also makes use of information technology to build a safer aviation system to support pilots and air traffic controllers. The FAA is assisting in defining requirements and actions to enact many of the safety standards. The Defense Department is expected to share in technology development, applying safety advances to military aircraft.

Initially AvSP identified eight technology strategies:

- Make every flight the equivalent of clear-day operations.
- Bring intelligent weather decision-making tools, including worldwide, real-time moving map displays, to every cockpit.
- Eliminate severe turbulence as an aviation hazard.
- Continuously track, diagnose, and restore the health of on-board systems, leading to self-healing and "refuse to crash" aircraft.
- Improve human and machine integration in design, operations, and maintenance.
- Monitor and assess all data from every flight for both known and unknown issues.
- Increase survivability when accidents do occur.
- Anticipate and prepare for future issues as the aviation system evolves.

One crucial enhancement is an advanced cockpit display that will use technologies such as global positioning system signals and terrain databases to give pilots a clear out-the-window picture, no matter what the weather or time of day. This synthetic vision concept includes digital video and infrared camera images, as well as data fed from microwave radar systems. The video and infrared images combine with computer-generated graphics to provide abundant visual cues during approaches and landings. A related goal is to devise sensors that will replace or exceed the capabilities of human vision, permitting an increase in the number of flights in poor weather, with the prospect of reduction in terminal delays and less costs for the airline industry and passengers.[14]

Aviation safety experts are also looking at the human side of accidents, developing models to better predict human error and working to improve training and other procedures for maintenance and flight crews. Accident-mitigation researchers are working to make accidents more survivable. AvSP drop tests of full-scale airplanes help engineers determine how to make aircraft seats, restraining systems, and structures better able to withstand crashes. Researchers are also developing new technologies to prevent in-flight fires and minimize fire hazards after an accident. Engineers are also developing on-board technologies to help planes monitor their own systems, including engines and airframes. The idea is to detect and diagnose abnormalities, then fix them before they become critical.[15]

IN THE AFTERMATH OF SEPTEMBER 11, 2001

Aircraft safety and security assumed enormous importance in the immediate aftermath of the September 11, 2001, terrorist attacks on the World Trade Center in New York City and on the Pentagon just outside Washington, D.C. The sight of the trade towers burning and then collapsing evoked similar feelings for viewers as those experienced by radio listeners learning of the Japanese attack on Pearl Harbor on December 7, 1941. Unlike that time, an era without pervasive television and 24-hour news chan-

nels, images of the destruction were replayed constantly, amplifying emotions and fears. But this was a new kind of war: hard to define, hard to escape, and hard to fight.

Different in kind and scope from World War II, or the uneasy decades-long period that followed it, the antiterrorist campaign seemed unlikely to spur the development of large air- or spacecraft as a means of defense or deterrence. President George W. Bush warned that this was a conflict likely to last for years, albeit with secret victories and hidden costs. Given the decentralized nature of the ongoing threat, the technologies most likely to see deployment appeared more personal: smaller sensors to detect traditional or nuclear munitions; automated lightweight reconnaissance aircraft to track the movement of guerillas and contraband; and equipment or gear that could sniff out, discourage, or prevent biological and chemical attack. Given its experience and expertise, NASA could play a role in creation and refinement of such technologies.

"Langley does not exist independently," says Jeremiah Creedon, former Center Director of Langley. "We cannot ignore external influences, whether they're political, geopolitical, or economic. We're no longer a self-contained entity, not even to the extent we were ten years ago. We'll maintain our identity, but outside our gates is an entire world that we're part of."

Under NASA Administrator Sean O'Keefe, the NASA Office of Aerospace Technology (OAT) announced early in 2002 a post-terrorist-attack policy addressing solutions to what it called "critical issues in aeronautics." The blueprint identified four elements on which NASA will focus in the years ahead: refinement of digital airspace, so that private aircraft will be easier and safer to fly; the development of revolutionary vehicles able to transit easily between air and space, with minimal environmental impact; strengthened security and safety technologies; and contributing to a state-of-the-art, educated workforce.

The OAT believes that an enhanced digital airspace will provide precise knowledge to pilots and controllers of air traffic, access to detailed terrain maps, and up-to-the minute weather forecasts to make flying as safe as possible. Creation of revolutionary vehicles should enable unprecedented levels of mobility and safety while safeguarding the environment and quelling the noise usually associated with airports. New security technologies are intended to protect life and property from hazards and malicious intent, while support of science and mathematics education at all levels should enable workers to more rapidly adapt to the use of complex technology in a world of rapid advancement.

"Aeronautics technology has not reached its limits," says Sam Venneri, former Chief Technologist at NASA Headquarters. "Revolutionary advances in materials, information technology, complex engineering systems, and much more will enable aviation to surpass the achievements of the first century of flight."[16]

NASA Headquarters and Langley continue to believe that advanced aerospace vehicles remain central to national security, transportation, mobility, freedom, and quality of life. Continued viability of aviation will not occur through evolutionary or near-term approaches

Biologically inspired aircraft in the Basic Aerodynamics Research Tunnel.

ASA Langley photo no. EL-2000-00581

Biologically inspired micro air vehicle wing.

NASA Langley photo no. EL-2001-00164

alone, some argue, but through thoughtful development of revolutionary, long-term approaches that make use of emerging technologies. Significant advances in biotechnology, nanotechnology, and information technology may open the door to a new era in aircraft development with designs that could prove radically different from time-honored versions. If so, the long-held dream of personal aviation modeled on avian physiology could finally become a reality.

The blended wing body model mounted in the Compact Range Facility for antenna pattern measurements.

NASA Langley photo no. EL-1998-00075

BEYOND THE FIRST ONE HUNDRED YEARS

Perhaps the bird-loving Saracen of Constantinople, who died in the 11th century while trying to fly with a stiffened cloak, or Abbot Damina of Tungland, injured in an attempt to fly with cloth wings from the walls of Stirling Castle in Scotland in 1507, were simply too enthusiastic too early. According to NASA planners, future aircraft may evolve into more bird-like craft, able to quickly adapt to the constantly varying conditions of flight, rapidly responding to differing conditions with unprecedented levels of aerodynamic efficiency. Embedded sensors will act like the nerves in a bird's wing and will measure the pressure over an entire wing surface. The response to these measurements will direct the craft's actuators, which will function similarly to a bird's wing muscles. Just as a bird instinctively uses different feathers on its wings to control its flight, the actuators will subtly change the shape of an aircraft's wings to continually optimize flight. Active-flow controllers will help mitigate adverse aircraft motions when turbulent air conditions are encountered.

Intelligent systems composed of these sensors, actuators, microprocessors, and adaptive controls will essentially provide the airborne equivalent of a central nervous system. Such vehicles should be able to monitor their own performance, environment, and even their pilots to improve safety and fuel efficiency and minimize airframe noise. Also incorporated within their structures will be systems that allow for safe takeoffs and landings from short airfields, which will enable access to the country's more than 5,400 rural and regional airports.[1]

Morphing Project Manager Anna McGowan examines actuators on a model.

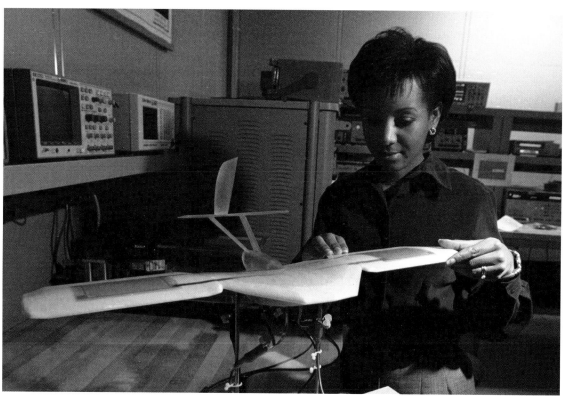

Langley Office of External Affairs photo archives

To explore these advanced vehicle concepts and exploit next-generation technologies, Langley researchers are using advanced computer analysis to model and predict the best locations for sensors and actuators. Specific technology areas of study include ground-to-flight scaling, reliability-based designs, adaptive flow control, robust controls, and autonomic vehicle functions.[2]

"Tried-and-true evolutionary technologies will not lead to revolutionary products. Revolutionary goals require high risk technologies," says Langley chief scientist Dennis Bushnell. "That's the only way to achieve the true breakthroughs. You've never been there before and you do not know how it's going to work out. You manage the risk by working multiple possibilities. One or more could pan out. If so, taking a calculated risk, you can end up with a pretty impressive outcome."

PRACTICAL SPACE

One of the riskiest technologies may be that of hypersonic flight or traveling over five times the speed of sound. At altitudes flown by jetliners, sound travels at close to 660 miles per hour, or Mach 1. A hypersonic plane could fly from New York to Los Angeles in under one hour. But the goal of current NASA hypersonic research is geared not to terrestrial concerns but to orbital ones: reusable space launch vehicles that would be strong but lightweight, carry more payload, and require far less turnaround time than conventional chemically powered rocket-launch systems.

As the lead for technology development for the NASA Hyper-X/X-43 program—intended to lead to a prototype craft that could fly 7 to 10 times the speed of sound—Langley tested in 1999 a full-scale hypersonic engine model in

NASA Langley photo no. EL-1997-00036

Model of Hyper-X on Pegasus booster rocket being installed in the 20-Inch Mach 6 Tunnel.

NASA Langley photo no. EL-1996-00096

Large scale scramjet concept demonstration model in the 8-Foot High-Temperature Tunnel.

John Simmons checking a hypersonic inlet prior to testing in the Arc-Heated Scramjet Test Facility.

NASA Langley photo no. EL-1998-00229

the Langley 8-Foot High-Temperature Tunnel. Langley engineers had previously validated the concept of hypersonic propulsion in Center tunnels: a scramjet, or supersonic combustion ramjet, with no moving parts that uses the speed of the aircraft to induce combustion. Combustion in a scramjet occurs when compressed air traveling at supersonic speed through the combuster itself ignites onboard hydrogen fuel, eliminating the need for stored oxygen used by conventional rocket systems. And because oxygen tanks are not required, the subsequent reduced weight allows the aircraft to carry more payload.

A milestone in the project was the development of a 12-foot-long aircraft model, the X-43A, that would be flown piggyback on a Pegasus booster rocket (provided by the firm Orbital Sciences

Corp.) to acquire enough speed to trigger combustion. But in an initial X-43A test flight over the Pacific Ocean off the California coast in June 2001, an apparent catastrophic structural failure in the booster caused the range safety officers to order the immediate destruction of the booster rocket and the X-43A model. Once a study group has issued its report on the mishap, current plans call for the Hyper-X program to continue and test flights to recommence.[3]

Langley's role in the NASA space science enterprise was also enhanced with the involvement of a team of Center scientists and engineers who have worked with the Jet Propulsion Laboratory in California on the Mars Odyssey project. The 2001 *Mars Odyssey* is part of the NASA Mars Exploration Program, which is a long-term effort of robotic exploration of the Red Planet. Mars launches typically are scheduled every 26 months, when the alignment of Earth and Mars in their orbits around the Sun allows spacecraft to travel between the two planets with the least amount of energy. The 2001 *Mars Odyssey* launched on April 7, 2001, and arrived at Mars on October 23, 2001.

Odyssey's primary science mission began February 2002 and is slated to continue through August 2004. For the first time, the mission will map the amount and distribution of chemical elements and minerals that make up the Martian surface, and record radiation levels in low-Mars orbit to determine the risk to any future human explorers. In an initial and significant find, announced in late May 2002, the spacecraft detected what appears to be large subsurface amounts of hydrogen, most likely in the form of water ice, near the planet's surface. If the presence of water is indeed confirmed by future missions, either robotic or human, the discovery could prove momentous for the nascent field of astrobiology.

During and after the science mission, the *Odyssey* orbiter will also support other missions in the Mars Exploration program. It will act as a communications

Third stage of Mars Pathfinder is attached in a clean room (left).

Model of probe for 2001 Mars mission tested by Langley researchers (top right).

Mars viewed by the Hubble Telescope in June 1999 (bottom right).

NASA Kennedy photo no. KSC-96PC-1267

NASA Langley photo no. EL-1998-00217

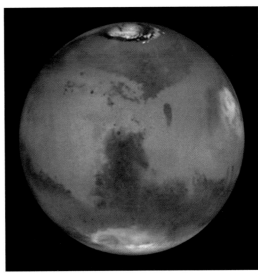

GPN photo no. GPN-2000-000923

An image of the Mangola Fossa, a deep trough on the Martian surface taken by *Mars Odyssey* in May 2002.

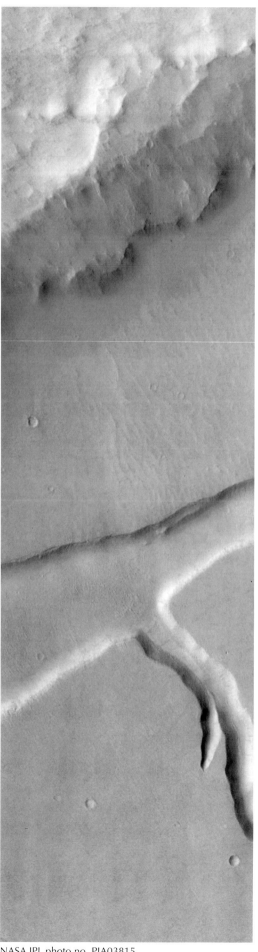

NASA JPL photo no. PIA03815

relay for American and international landers, including the next mission in the NASA Mars Program, the Mars Exploration Rovers, which are slated to launch in 2003. Scientists and engineers will also use Odyssey data to identify potential landing sites for future Mars missions.[5]

Langley participation enabled the spacecraft to literally surf the waves of the Martian atmosphere in a process called "aerobraking," a technique wherein an orbiting spacecraft brushes against the top of an atmosphere. The friction of the atmosphere against the surface of the spacecraft slows down the craft, lowering its orbital altitude. Attached solar panels are used to provide the maximum drag in a symmetrical position, allowing some additional control as the spacecraft passes through the atmosphere.

Instead of using onboard jets and propellant to adjust a spacecraft's orbit, aerobraking uses the atmosphere as both a brake and a steering wheel. The technique, however, shares more elements with sailing than with driving: successful aerobraking depends upon precise navigation, knowledge of weather, and a solid understanding of the forces the craft can withstand. Atmospheric drag—the friction a spacecraft experiences as it passes through the top layer of the atmosphere—reduces spacecraft velocity. Each pass brings the spacecraft to a lower altitude. Repeated drag passes, as they are called, are conducted to shape the spacecraft's trajectory from its initial elliptical orbit into the desired circular orbit. The design of each drag pass is carefully worked out by navigators, spacecraft engineers, and scientists who measure the results of the preceding pass,

The Langley Aerobraking Team on day 75 of vehicle aerobraking.

NASA Langley photo no. EL-2002-00270

read measurements, and estimate the height and density of the atmosphere, predict the atmosphere's effect on the spacecraft's structure, and determine the best entry and exit points to achieve the orbital geometry required for the mission.[4]

Aerobraking is extremely challenging but worth it, say mission engineers, because it eliminates the heavy load of extra propellant that would otherwise be needed to place the spacecraft in its desired orbit. This approach reduced the *Odyssey's* long elliptical orbit into a shorter, 2-hour circular orbit of approximately 400 kilometers (about 250 miles) altitude. This positioned the spacecraft in a lower orbit for scientific observations.[6]

The Langley Odyssey team has supported the Jet Propulsion Laboratory by monitoring the aerodynamics and the heating of the spacecraft as it passes through the thin atmosphere of Mars. One of Langley's tasks has been to

determine how deeply the orbiter should penetrate the Martian atmosphere on each pass. If the passes are too deep, the solar panels could burn up; if the passes are too shallow, the mission could end up in a useless orbit.

"These are very challenging and exciting missions," said Dick Powell, Langley technical lead for Mars *Odyssey*, who headed a group of 18 Langley and George Washington University researchers that monitored the aerobraking phase of the *Odyssey* mission. "There are many uncertainties about Mars. The atmosphere is primarily carbon dioxide as opposed to Earth's atmosphere that is primarily nitrogen. So we have to figure out a way to modify all our computational tools to apply to these vehicles. Also, there is no infrastructure, no global positioning satellites, no meteorological satellites, so we have to allow a great deal of margin in these spacecraft to handle the unknown."[7]

BEYOND EXPECTATIONS

Throughout its history, Langley has made a habit of going beyond the technologically expected. In over three-quarters of a century, the Center's methodical precision has brought about beneficial change to both aircraft and spacecraft. Langley led or was a major participant in aerospace innovation amidst an astonishing century-long explosion of science and technology.

Despite a growing focus on applied research, former Center Director Creedon believes the coming decade could offer Langley more rather than less opportunity. Although large programs on the order of Mercury, Gemini, Apollo, or Viking do not seem to be in the cards, modest ones aimed at significant technological impact may indeed have the desired results. It may be of greater benefit, he believes, not to be constrained by large, complex programs with endpoints too carefully defined.

"For my first three years as a researcher I did not really talk to anybody. They shoved problems under my door. I shoved the answers back out," Creedon says. "When a big hunk of the Center was working on focused programs, the individual researcher was not as free to shape the goals sought. Their innovation came in *how* they achieved those goals. Researchers got used to having objectives specified. The right balance was lost. Too much time was spent on a problem the parameters of which were already spelled out. Less time was spent on what problems *should* be solved. Creativity suffered."

Historian James Hansen worries that overemphasis on applied research may,

however, miss the research point. The movement away from basic to more focused research could depress and not encourage innovation. "One might wonder whether NASA engineers and scientists of the 1960s and 1970s, if situated in such a strict service-oriented environment so imprisoned by proprietary interests and an accountant's bottom line, could ever have been thoughtful enough to conceptualize a machine as revolutionary as National Transonic Facility [at Langley Research Center] in the first place," Hansen points out. "Without a more adventurous approach to attacking fundamental problems, aerodynamic progress through the 20th century could never have advanced the state of the art nearly as rapidly—or as incredibly successfully—as it has actually done."[8]

One field of study within Langley that may blur the distinction between basic and applied research is atmospheric sciences. Although strictly speaking, atmospheric sciences research is not applied; its results can be, as in contributions to actions taken to reduce the threat from chlorofluorocarbons to Earth's protective ozone layer. The Center's atmospheric scientists have made major contributions to atmospheric chemistry and the processes that affect weather and climate change. Water vapor, in the form of droplets or clouds can, for example, trap solar radiation, while volcanic eruptions can release sunlight-blocking pollutants. More recently, Langley scientists have made major strides in determining the ways clouds mitigate and influence planetary temperatures.

"We now have a 20-year record of understanding the energy balance and the Earth-Sun interaction: How much solar

Dr. Larry B. Petway makes final adjustments to an instrument for the Lidar Atmospheric Sensing Experiment (LASE).

NASA Langley photo no. EL-1996-00202

Model of Boeing 777 in the National Transonic Facility at Langley.

NASA Langley photo no. EL-2001-00041

radiation comes in and warms Earth and how much is reflected out," says Leonard McMaster, director of Langley's Atmospheric Sciences Competency. "Our atmospheric research began as an attempt to understand the fluid in which airplanes flew. Now we're making major contributions in terms of understanding the mechanisms of climate change. With the instruments we're putting up over the next several years we should be able to develop a much more comprehensive understanding of the dynamics of these complicated atmospheric processes."

Launches are still planned for the constellation of satellites that comprise the ambitious Earth Observing System (EOS), part of the program known as Mission to Planet Earth. Designed to monitor the atmosphere on a continuing basis, EOS sensors will send back a steady, comprehensive stream of information about atmospheric workings. Atmospheric sciences researchers and

their systems-engineering and electronics-research colleagues at Langley are playing a prominent and ongoing role in the development of complex EOS instrumentation.

BEYOND THE BEACH

What might a "new" NASA Langley be like? One model for innovation could be a public-private partnership involving Langley, industry, and universities. The National Institute of Aerospace (NIA), announced in the fall of 2001, will be headquartered at Langley with the goal of developing "revolutionary new technologies" as its first promotional brochure states. The Institute will have dedicated facilities near the Center. In addition to promoting and providing graduate education in aerospace science and engineering, the NIA would also "incubate, stimulate, and commercialize" Langley-derived intellectual property

Langley staff members share the excitement of science.

NASA Langley photo no. EL-2001-00342

and inventions, as well as those of its partners.

Langley is also engaged in several programs to bring its expertise directly to classrooms, from elementary schools to universities. The Center, for example, manages an instructional television series that joins classrooms with NASA researchers in support of national math, science, and technology education standards. Students learn how NASA engineers and scientists apply math, science, and technology directly to their work and how these disciplines incorporate creativity, critical thinking, and problem-solving skills.

"Ideas sustain innovation. While NASA is hardly the only source of ideas, it has been the source of a great many good ones, with unmatched facilities and researchers," contends Deborah Douglas, the curator of science and technology at the MIT Museum in Cambridge, Massachusetts. "Does that mean that

everything that comes out of NASA is great? No. But NASA in the 1990s did continue to set the aerospace agenda. The result was support for areas of great value to American society."

In this millennium, the issues confronting NASA and Langley appear likely to be those more resistant to short-term resolution. Improving the speed, structure, and landing characteristics of a fabric-covered biplane was accomplished in a relatively short period of time; devising practical, economical, environmentally neutral designs for working supersonic and hypersonic airplanes is far more difficult and time-consuming.

It is becoming more difficult to separate the word "aero" from "space." At Langley and elsewhere new generations of aerospace engineers are beginning to consider the types of craft that, in coming decades, will breathe and fly through air and ply the vacuum of space. Like their

8

Hyper-X model undergoing tests in a wind tunnel at Langley.

Langley Office of External Affairs photo archives

Hyper-X model and rocket mounted on research aircraft in preparation for test flight.

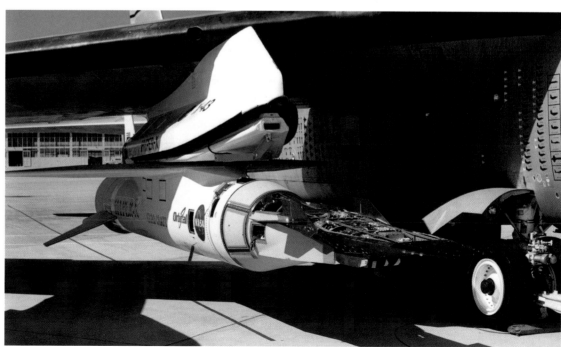

Langley Office of External Affairs photo archives

Crafting Flight

predecessors, this generation of Langley engineers and theoreticians will be confronted by seemingly intractable difficulties. Perhaps they will be the ones who figure out how to beat the gravity-well problem—the difficulty of inexpensively boosting payloads and people into orbit.

Budget cutting and program cutbacks have also taken a toll, as talented younger researchers abandon government service for more lucrative and potentially more rewarding work in the private sector. The danger of continued anemic budgetary support for NASA aeronautics research, warns Robert Ash, eminent scholar of aerospace engineering and associate vice president for research and graduate studies at Old Dominion University in Norfolk, Virginia, is that core expertise may be irretrievably lost. Although new hires may be bright and motivated, they must earn their experience—a process around which there are no shortcuts. Still, Ash believes, aeronautics research can and will offer much to the Nation. He agrees that research-driven technological convergence could usher in an entirely new era.

"Aviation is poised similarly as was the computer industry in the 1980s, when the personal computer took off: fewer higher end products and more distributed ones," Ash says. "Eventually we'll have a personalized aircraft system and personalized aircraft: a smart box that can land itself. NASA is the only organization capable of shepherding such a revolutionary change in personal transportation."

Basic research appears unlikely to fade as much as supporters fear. Times may have changed, and monies more carefully parceled out, but the human need to understand and to explore seems just as strong as ever.

The results of basic research tend eventually to be applied in practical realms—as were, for example, explorations of quantum physics in the 1920s and 1930s that led eventually to the development of personal computers, compact and digital video disk players, and the Internet. Often the practitioners themselves have a hard time understanding or predicting the ultimate use of their ruminations. Take Langley researcher Richard Whitcomb, for instance, whose aircraft area rule helped to make practical jet flight a reality with trailblazing research into supersonic flight effects on airplane designs.

"Nobody in the United States in the 1930s realized that the jet would be the vehicle on which people would eventually fly. Nobody," says former NASA chief historian Roger Launius. "It takes a unique person in a uniquely appropriate situation to pick the innovation that will revolutionize things. It's almost impossible to institutionalize it. But it has happened, as with Dick Whitcomb [at Langley], a rare genius who can see things no one else can."

One wonders what the Wright brothers would have made of supersonic transports, supercomputers, Moon shots, and planetary flybys. One hopes that the enterprising pair would have approved of the spirit of adventure and the thirst for knowledge such endeavors provoke. Seen from a longer distance, the progression of flight from the spray-drenched sands of a cold North Carolina beach into an even colder interplanetary void was epic and almost unbelievable. After all, in fewer than three generations, the drone

A Cirrus SSR-20 cockpit with advanced general aviation technology.

NASA Langley photo no. EL-2000-00009

Langley research aircraft *Aries* during Synthetic Vision Systems test in Colorado in 2001.

NASA Langley photo no. EL-2002-00028

Active volcanic eruption on Jupiter's moon Io in an image taken by *Galileo* spacecraft in 2000.

NASA JPL photo no. PIA02550

of wooden propellers had been drowned out in the roar of jets and in the Earth-shaking fire of rockets.

One day Langley could well be engaged in research relating to a crewed mission to Mars or helping to design craft that will conduct scientific research from crewed outposts on the satellites of Jupiter and Saturn. Or perhaps the Center will concentrate on projects closer to home, figuring ways to fly ever faster and more safely through Earth's atmosphere and designing the next generation of automated, uncrewed space probes. No matter what areas of research the next generations of aerospace engineers and scientists explore, it seems certain that Langley will continue to do what it has traditionally done best: figure out what works, and works better, and then make sure the improvements find their way in due course onto the machines that fly in the air and travel through space.

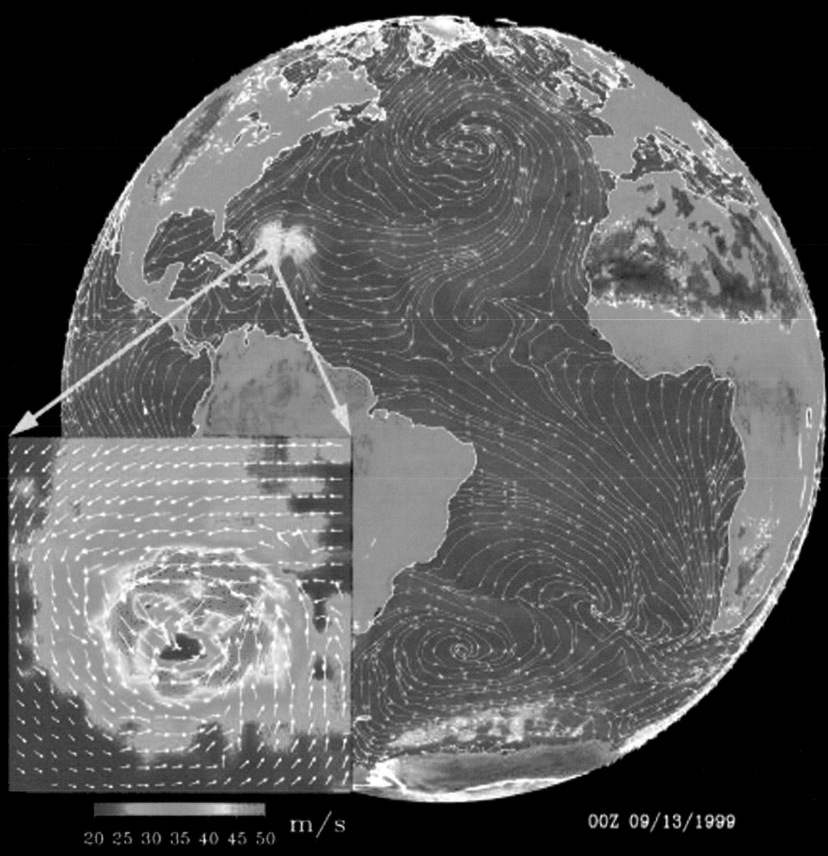

Satellite image of winds over oceans.

m/s

20 25 30 35 40 45 50

00Z 09/13/1999

0 1 2 3 4 5 6 7 8 9 10 11 12 13 14 15 16 17

Langley Office of External Affairs photo archives

Wind Speed (m/s)

FOOTNOTES

CHAPTER ONE: CRAVING FLIGHT

1. Serge Bramly, with translation by Sian Reynolds. *Leonardo: Discovering the Life of Leonardo da Vinc.* HarperCollins Publishers, New York, NY, 1991.

2. Ibid.

3. Ibid.

4. Ibid.

5. Walter Boyne, Terry Gwynn-Jones and Valerie Moolman. *How Things Work: Flight.* Time-Life Books Inc./St. Remy Press. Alexandria, VA, 1990.

6. Ibid.

7. Reginald Carpenter, Peter Kalla-Bishop, Kenneth Munson and Robert Wyatt. *Powered Vehicles: A Historical Review.* Crown Publishers Inc. New York, NY, 1974.

8. Walter Boyne, Terry Gwynn-Jones and Valerie Moolman. *How Things Work: Flight.* Time-Life Books Inc./St. Remy Press. Alexandria, VA, 1990.

9. Ibid.

10. Ibid.

11. Ibid.

12. Ibid.

13. Ibid.

14. Ibid.

15. Ibid.

16. Microsoft® Encarta® Encyclopedia 2001. © 1993-2000 Microsoft Corporation.

17. Ibid.

18. Walter Boyne, Terry Gwynn-Jones and Valerie Moolman. *How Things Work: Flight.* Time-Life Books Inc./St. Remy Press. Alexandria, VA, 1990.

19. Ibid.

20. Ibid.

21. Microsoft® Encarta® Encyclopedia 2001. © 1993-2000 Microsoft Corporation.

22. Tom D. Crouch. *The Bishop's Boys: A Life of Wilbur and Orville Wright.* W.W. Norton and Company. New York, NY, 1989.

23. Ibid.

24. Ibid.

25. Ibid.

26. Ibid.

27. Ibid.

28. Ibid.

29. Ibid.

30. Ibid.

31. Ibid.

32. Ibid.

33. Ibid.

34. Ibid.

35. Ibid.

36. Ibid.

37. Ibid.

38. Ibid.

39. James R. Hansen. *Engineer In Charge: A History of the Langley Aeronautical Laboratory, 1917–1958.* NASA /Scientific and Technical Information Office. Washington, D.C., 1987.

Chapter Two: A Laboratory for Flight

1. James R. Hansen. *Engineer In Charge: A History of the Langley Aeronautical Laboratory, 1917–1958.* NASA /Scientific and Technical Information Office. Washington, D.C., 1987.

2. Ibid.

3. Ibid.

4. Ibid.

5. Tom D. Crouch. *The Bishop's Boys: A Life of Wilbur and Orville Wright.* W.W. Norton and Company. New York, NY. 1989.

6. James R. Hansen. *Engineer In Charge: A History of the Langley Aeronautical Laboratory, 1917–1958.* NASA /Scientific and Technical Information Office. Washington, D.C., 1987.

7. Ibid.

8. Ibid.

9. Ibid.

10. Ibid.

11. Ibid.

12. Ibid.

13. Ibid.

14. Ibid.

15. Ibid.

16. NASA Langley Library tape archives

17. Ibid.

18. James R. Hansen. *Engineer In Charge: A History of the Langley Aeronautical Laboratory, 1917-1958.* NASA /Scientific and Technical Information Office. Washington, D.C., 1987.

19. Ibid.

20. John Becker. *The High-Speed Frontier: Case Histories of Four NACA Programs 1920–1950.* U.S. Government Printing Office: NASA SP-445, 1980.

Chapter Three: Reinventing the Plane

1. Hansen, James R. *Engineer In Charge: A History of the Langley Aeronautical Laboratory, 1917–1958.* U.S. Government Printing Office: NASA SP-4305, 1987.

2. Ibid.

3. Smithsonian Institution: National Air and Space Museum. *Milestones of Aviation.* Hugh Lauter Levin Associates, New York, N.Y., 1989.

4. Hansen, James R. *Engineer In Charge: A History of the Langley Aeronautical Laboratory, 1917–1958.* U.S. Government Printing Office: NASA SP-4305, 1987.

5. Ibid.

6. Ibid.

7. Ibid.

8. Becker, John. *The High-Speed Frontier: Case Histories of Four NACA Programs, 1920–1950.* U.S. Government Printing Office: NASA SP-445, 1980.

9. Hansen, James R. *Engineer In Charge: A History of the Langley Aeronautical Laboratory, 1917–1958.* U.S. Government Printing Office: NASA SP-4305, 1987.

10. Ibid.

11. Ibid.

12. Ibid.

13. Ibid.

14. Ibid.

15. Ibid.

16. Ibid.

17. Ibid.

18. Ibid.

19. Ibid.

20. Ibid.

21. Ibid.

22. Ibid.

23. Loftin, Laurence K., Jr. *Quest for Performance: The Evolution of Modern Aircraft.* U.S. Government Printing Office: NASA SP-468, 1985.

24. Ibid.

25. Ibid.

26. Hansen, James R. *Engineer In Charge: A History of the Langley Aeronautical Laboratory, 1917–1958.* U.S. Government Printing Office: NASA SP-4305, 1987.

27. Ibid.

28. Ibid.

29. Ibid.

30. Ibid.

31. Smithsonian Institution: National Air and Space Museum. *Milestones of Aviation.* Hugh Lauter Levin Associates, New York, N.Y., 1989.

32. NASA Langley Library archives.

CHAPTER FOUR: SWORDS AND PLOWSHARES

1. Hansen, James R. *Engineer In Charge: A History of the Langley Aeronautical Laboratory, 1917–1958.* U.S. Government Printing Office: NASA SP-4305, 1987.

2. Ibid.

3. Ibid.

4. Ibid.

5. Ibid.

6. Loftin, Laurence K., Jr. *Quest for Performance: The Evolution of Modern Aircraft.* U.S. Government Printing Office: NASA SP-468, 1985.

7. Hansen, James R. *Engineer In Charge: A History of the Langley Aeronautical Laboratory, 1917–1958.* U.S. Government Printing Office: NASA SP-4305, 1987.

8. Ibid.

9. Ibid.

10. Ibid.

11. Ibid.

12. Ibid.

13. Ibid.

14. Ibid.

15. Ibid.

16. Ibid.

17. Baals, Donald D. and Corliss, William R. *Wind Tunnels of NASA.* U.S. Government Printing Office: NASA SP-440, 1981.

18. Ibid.

19. Ibid.

20. Hansen, James R. *Engineer In Charge: A History of the Langley Aeronautical Laboratory, 1917–1958.* U.S. Government Printing Office: NASA SP-4305, 1987.

21. Baals, Donald D. and Corliss, William R. *Wind Tunnels of NASA.* U.S. Government Printing Office: NASA SP-440, 1981.

22. Hansen, James R. *Engineer In Charge: A History of the Langley Aeronautical Laboratory, 1917–1958.* U.S. Government Printing Office: NASA SP-4305, 1987.

23. Ibid.

24. Smithsonian Institution: National Air and Space Museum. *Milestones of Aviation.* Hugh Lauter Levin Associates, New York, N.Y., 1989.

CHAPTER FIVE: BEYOND THE HOME PLANET

1. Hansen, James R. *Engineer In Charge: A History of the Langley Aeronautical Laboratory, 1917–1958.* U.S. Government Printing Office: NASA SP-4305, 1987.

2. Ibid.

3. Ibid.

4. Ibid.

5. Ibid.

CHAPTER SIX: EXPERTISE APPLIED

1. Henry, Keith and Nolan-Proxmire, Don. NASA Langley/Headquarters news release 96-154. October 1, 1996.

2. Ibid.

3. Ibid.

4. Henry, Keith and Patrick, Hal. NASA Langley news release 99-068. September 10, 1999.

5. Ibid.

6. Braukus, Michael; Hinz, Sue and Rink, Chris. NASA Langley/Headquarters news release 02-014. February 21, 2002.

7. Ibid.

8. Ibid.

9. Ibid.

CHAPTER SEVEN: REDEFINING ROLES

1. NASA Advisory Council's Federal Laboratory Review Task Force. February 1995.

2. Ibid.

3. Hansen, James. E-mail notes to author. February 1, 2002.

4. Ibid.

5. Ibid.

6. Schultz, James. "HSR Leaves Legacy Of Spinoffs." Aerospace America. September 1999.

7. Ibid.

8. Ibid.

9. NASA Langley fact sheet FS-1996-05-01-LaRC. May 1996.

10. Henry, Keith. NASA Langley news release 97-095. August 2, 1997.

11. Ibid.

12. Braukus, Michael; Henry, Keith and Sheehan, John. NASA Langley news release 02-23. May 14, 2002.

13. Finneran, Michael. NASA Langley news release 97-042. June 3, 1997.

14. Ibid.

15. http://avsp.larc.nasa.gov/

16. Braukus, Michael. NASA Headquarters new release 0223. Feb. 5, 2002.

CHAPTER EIGHT: FURTHER OUT

1. Bushnell, D.M. *On Civil Aviation Futures.* The Aeronautical Journal of the Royal Aeronautical Society. October 2001.

2. Ibid.

3. Johnson, Fredrick; Rink, Chris; Williams, Leslie. NASA Langley Dryden news release 01-43a. June 18, 2001.

4. http://mars.jpl.nasa.gov/odyssey/overview/index.html

5. http://mars.jpl.nasa.gov/odyssey/mission/aerobraking.html

6. Ibid.

7. Ibid.

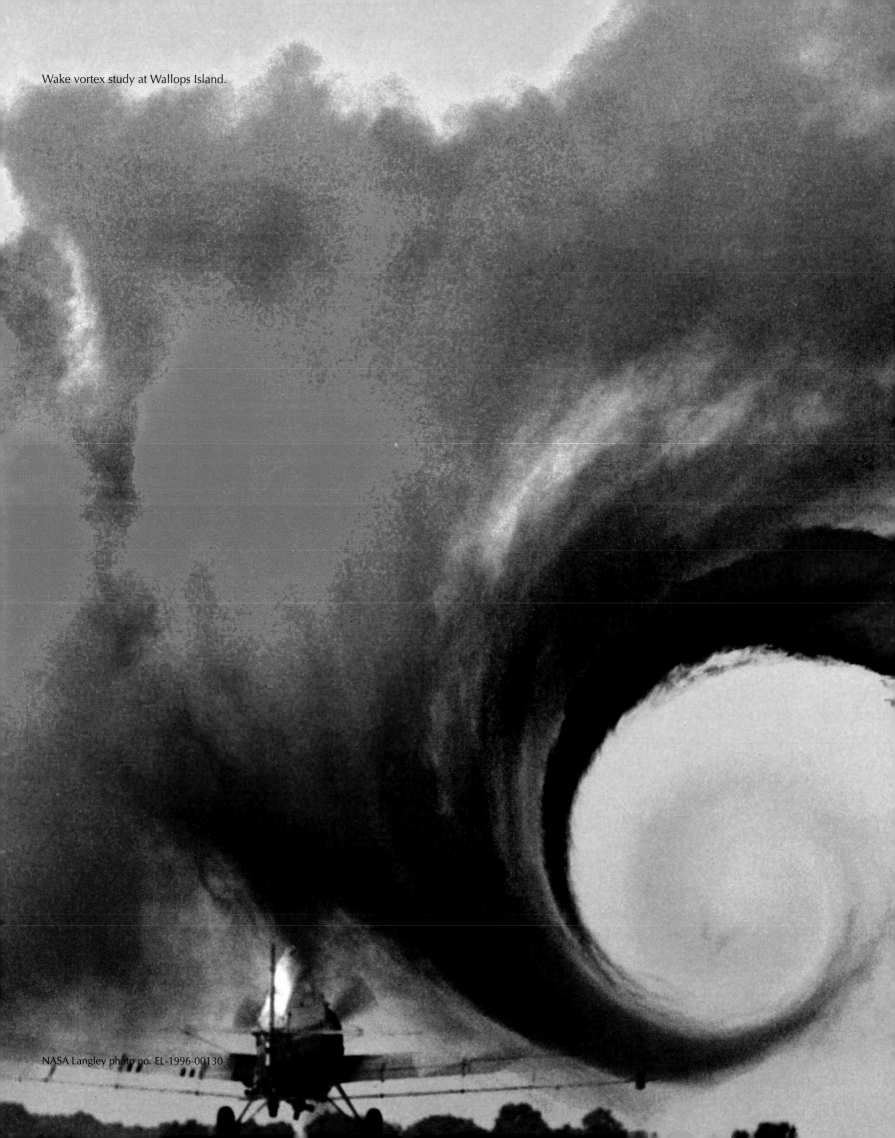

Wake vortex study at Wallops Island.

NASA Langley photo no. EL-1996-00130

BIBLIOGRAPHY

Engineer In Charge: A History of the Langley Aeronautical Laboratory, 1917-1958,
by James R. Hansen. NASA /Scientific and Technical Information Office.
Washington, D.C., 1987.

How Things Work: Flight, by Walter Boyne, Terry Gwynn-Jones and Valerie Moolman.
Time-Life Books Inc./St. Remy Press. Alexandria, VA, 1990.

Leonardo: Discovering the Life of Leonardo da Vinci, by Serge Bramly, with translation
by Sian Reynolds. HarperCollins Publishers, New York, NY, 1991.

Powered Vehicles: A Historical Review, by Reginald Carpenter, Peter Kalla-Bishop,
Kenneth Munson and Robert Wyatt. Crown Publishers Inc. New York, NY, 1974.

The Bishop's Boys: A Life of Wilbur and Orville Wright, by Tom D. Crouch. W.W. Norton
and Company. New York, NY, 1989.

The High-Speed Frontier: Case Histories of Four NACA Programs 1920–1950,
by John Becker. U.S. Government Printing Office: NASA SP-445, 1980.

Spaceflight Revolution: NASA Langley Research Center From Sputnik To Apollo,
by James R. Hansen. U.S. Government Printing Office: NASA SP-4308, 1995.

Wind Tunnels of NASA, by Donald D. Baals and William R. Corliss. U.S. Government
Printing Office: NASA SP-440, 1981.

Flap edge of Energy
Efficient Transport in
Langley Low Turbulence
Pressure Tunnel.

NASA Langley photo no. EL-1998-00167.

NASA History Series

Reference Works, NASA SP-4000

Grimwood, James M. *Project Mercury: A Chronology.* (NASA SP-4001, 1963).

Grimwood, James M., and Barton C. Hacker, with Peter J. Vorzimmer. *Project Gemini Technology and Operations: A Chronology.* (NASA SP-4002, 1969).

Link, Mae Mills. *Space Medicine in Project Mercury.* (NASA SP-4003, 1965).

Astronautics and Aeronautics, 1963: Chronology of Science, Technology, and Policy. (NASA SP-4004, 1964).

Astronautics and Aeronautics, 1964: Chronology of Science, Technology, and Policy. (NASA SP-4005, 1965).

Astronautics and Aeronautics, 1965: Chronology of Science, Technology, and Policy. (NASA SP-4006, 1966).

Astronautics and Aeronautics, 1966: Chronology of Science, Technology, and Policy. (NASA SP-4007, 1967).

Astronautics and Aeronautics, 1967: Chronology of Science, Technology, and Policy. (NASA SP-4008, 1968).

Ertel, Ivan D., and Mary Louise Morse. *The Apollo Spacecraft: A Chronology, Volume I, Through November 7, 1962.* (NASA SP-4009, 1969).

Morse, Mary Louise, and Jean Kernahan Bay. *The Apollo Spacecraft: A Chronology, Volume II, November 8, 1962–January 20, 1966.* (NASA SP-4009, 1973).

Ertel, Ivan D., and Roland W. Newkirk, with Courtney G. Brooks. *The Apollo Spacecraft: A Chronology, Volume III, January 21, 1966–July 13, 1974.* (NASA SP-4009, 1978).

Astronautics and Aeronautics, 1968: Chronology of Science, Technology, and Policy. (NASA SP-4010, 1969).

Newkirk, Roland W., and Ivan D. Ertel, with Courtney G. Brooks. *Skylab: A Chronology.* (NASA SP-4011, 1977).

Van Nimmen, Jane, and Leonard C. Bruno, with Robert L. Rosholt. *NASA Historical Data Book, Volume I: NASA Resources, 1958–1968.* (NASA SP-4012, 1976, rep. ed. 1988).

Ezell, Linda Neuman, *NASA Historical Data Book, Volume II: Programs and Projects, 1958–1968.* (NASA SP-4012, 1988).

Ezell, Linda Neuman. *NASA Historical Data Book, Volume III: Programs and Projects, 1969–1978.* (NASA SP-4012, 1988).

Gawdiak, Ihor Y., with Helen Fedor. Compilers. *NASA Historical Data Book, Volume IV: NASA Resources, 1969–1978.* (NASA SP-4012, 1994).

Rumerman, Judy A. Compiler. *NASA Historical Data Book, 1979–1988: Volume V, NASA Launch Systems, Space Transportation, Human Spaceflight, and Space Science.* (NASA SP-4012, 1999).

Rumerman, Judy A. Compiler. *NASA Historical Data Book, Volume VI: NASA Space Applications, Aeronautics and Space Research and Technology, Tracking and Data Acquisition/Space Operations, Commercial Programs, and Resources, 1979–1988.* (NASA SP-2000-4012, 2000).

Astronautics and Aeronautics, 1969: Chronology of Science, Technology, and Policy. (NASA SP-4014, 1970).

Astronautics and Aeronautics, 1970: Chronology of Science, Technology, and Policy. (NASA SP-4015, 1972).

Astronautics and Aeronautics, 1971: Chronology of Science, Technology, and Policy. (NASA SP-4016, 1972).

Astronautics and Aeronautics, 1972: Chronology of Science, Technology, and Policy. (NASA SP-4017, 1974).

Astronautics and Aeronautics, 1973: Chronology of Science, Technology, and Policy. (NASA SP-4018, 1975).

Astronautics and Aeronautics, 1974: Chronology of Science, Technology, and Policy. (NASA SP-4019, 1977).

Astronautics and Aeronautics, 1975: Chronology of Science, Technology, and Policy. (NASA SP-4020, 1979).

Astronautics and Aeronautics, 1976: Chronology of Science, Technology, and Policy. (NASA SP-4021, 1984).

Astronautics and Aeronautics, 1977: Chronology of Science, Technology, and Policy. (NASA SP-4022, 1986).

Astronautics and Aeronautics, 1978: Chronology of Science, Technology, and Policy. (NASA SP-4023, 1986).

Astronautics and Aeronautics, 1979–1984: Chronology of Science, Technology, and Policy. (NASA SP-4024, 1988).

Astronautics and Aeronautics, 1985: Chronology of Science, Technology, and Policy. (NASA SP-4025, 1990).

Noordung, Hermann. *The Problem of Space Travel: The Rocket Motor.* Stuhlinger, Ernst, and J. D. Hunley, with Jennifer Garland. Editors. (NASA SP-4026, 1995).

Astronautics and Aeronautics, 1986–1990: A Chronology. (NASA SP-4027, 1997).

Astronautics and Aeronautics, 1990–1995: A Chronology. (NASA SP-2000-4028, 2000).

Orloff, Richard W. Compiler. *Apollo by the Numbers: A Statistical Reference.* (NASA SP-2000-4029, 2000).

MANAGEMENT HISTORIES, NASA SP-4100

Rosholt, Robert L. *An Administrative History of NASA, 1958–1963.* (NASA SP-4101, 1966).

Levine, Arnold S. *Managing NASA in the Apollo Era.* (NASA SP-4102, 1982).

Roland, Alex. *Model Research: The National Advisory Committee for Aeronautics, 1915–1958.* (NASA SP-4103, 1985).

Fries, Sylvia D. *NASA Engineers and the Age of Apollo.* (NASA SP-4104, 1992).

Glennan, T. Keith. *The Birth of NASA: The Diary of T. Keith Glennan.* J. D. Hunley. Editor. (NASA SP-4105, 1993).

Seamans, Robert C., Jr. *Aiming at Targets: The Autobiography of Robert C. Seamans, Jr.* (NASA SP-4106, 1966).

PROJECT HISTORIES, NASA SP-4200

Swenson, Loyd S., Jr., James M. Grimwood, and Charles C. Alexander. *This New Ocean: A History of Project Mercury.* (NASA SP-4201, 1966; rep. ed. 1998).

Green, Constance M., and Milton Lomask. *Vanguard: A History.* (NASA SP-4202, 1970; rep. ed. Smithsonian Institution Press, 1971).

Hacker, Barton C., and James M. Grimwood. *On Shoulders of Titans: A History of Project Gemini.* (NASA SP-4203, 1977, rep. ed., 2002).

Benson, Charles D. and William Barnaby Faherty. *Moonport: A History of Apollo Launch Facilities and Operations.* (NASA SP-4204, 1978).

Brooks, Courtney G., James M. Grimwood, and Loyd S. Swenson, Jr. *Chariots for Apollo: A History of Manned Lunar Spacecraft.* (NASA SP-4205, 1979).

Bilstein, Roger E. *Stages to Saturn: A Technological History of the Apollo/Saturn Launch Vehicles.* (NASA SP-4206, 1980, rep. ed. 1997).

Compton, W. David, and Charles D. Benson. *Living and Working in Space: A History of Skylab.* (NASA SP-4208, 1983).

Ezell, Edward Clinton, and Linda Neuman Ezell. *The Partnership: A History of the Apollo-Soyuz Test Project.* (NASA SP-4209, 1978).

Hall, R. Cargill. *Lunar Impact: A History of Project Ranger.* (NASA SP-4210, 1977).

Newell, Homer E. *Beyond the Atmosphere: Early Years of Space Science.* (NASA SP-4211, 1980).

Ezell, Edward Clinton, and Linda Neuman Ezell. *On Mars: Exploration of the Red Planet, 1958–1978.* (NASA SP-4212, 1984).

Pitts, John A. *The Human Factor: Biomedicine in the Manned Space Program to 1980.* (NASA SP-4213, 1985).

Compton, W. David. *Where No Man has Gone Before: A History of Apollo Lunar Exploration Missions.* (NASA SO-4214, 1989).

Naugle, John E. *First Among Equals: The Selection of NASA Space Science Experiments.* (NASA SP-4215, 1991).

Wallace, Lane E. *Airborne Trailblazer: Two Decades with NASA Langley's Boeing 737 Flying Laboratory.* (NASA P-4216, 1994).

Butrica, Andrew J. Editor. *Beyond the Ionosphere: Fifty Years of Satellite Communication.* (NASA SP-4217, 1997).

Butrica, Andrew J. *To See the Unseen: A History of Planetary Radar Astronomy.* (NASA SP-4218, 1996).

Mack, Pamela E. Editor. *From Engineering Science to Big Science: The NACA and NASA Collier Trophy Research Project Winners.* (NASA SP-4219, 1998).

Reed, R. Dale, with Darlene Lister. *Wingless Flight: The Lifting Body Story.* (NASA SP-4220, 1997).

Heppenheimer, T. A. *The Space Shuttle Decision: NASA's Search for a Reusable Space Vehicle.* (NASA SP-4221, 1999).

Hunley, J. D. Editor. *Toward Mach 2: The Douglas D-558 Program.* (NASA SP-4222, 1999).

Swanson, Glen E. Editor. *"Before this Decade is Out...": Personal Reflections on the Apollo Program.* (NASA SP-4223, 1999).

Tomayko, James E. *Computers Take Flight: A History of NASA's Pioneering Digital Fly-by-Wire Project.* (NASA SSP-2000-4224, 2000).

Morgan, Clay. *Shuttle-Mir: The U.S. and Russia Share History's Highest Stage.* (NASA SP-2001-4225, 2001).

Mudgway, Douglas J. U*plink/Downlink: A History of the Deep Space Network.* (NASA SP-2002-4227, 2002).

Center Histories, NASA SP-4300

Rosenthal, Alfred. *Venture into Space: Early Years of Goddard Space Flight Center.* (NASA SP-4301, 1985).

Hartman, Edwin, P. *Adventures in Research: A History of Ames Research Center, 1940–1965.* (NASA SP-4302, 1970).

Hallion, Richard P. *On the Frontier: Flight Research at Dryden, 1946–1981.* (NASA SP-4303, 1984).

Muenger, Elizabeth A. *Searching the Horizon: A History of Ames Research Center, 1940–1976.* (NASA SP-4304, 1985).

Hansen, James R. *Spaceflight Revolution: NASA Langley Research Center from Sputnik to Apollo.* (NASA SP-4308, 1995).

Wallace, Lane E. *Flights of Discovery: 50 Years at the NASA Dryden Flight Research Center.* (NASA SP-4309, 1996).

Herring, Mack R. *Way Station to Space: A History of the John C. Stennis Space Center.* (NASA SP-4310, 1997).

Wallace, Harold D., Jr. *Wallops Station and the Creation of the American Space Program.* (NASA SP-4311, 1997).

Wallace, Lane E. *Dreams, Hopes, Realities: NASA's Goddard Space Flight Center, The First Forty Years.* (NASA SP-4312, 1999).

Dunar, Andrew J., and Stephen P. Waring. *Power to Explore: A History of the Marshall Space Flight Center.* (NASA SP-4313, 1999).

Bugos, Glenn E. *Atmosphere of Freedom: Sixty Years at the NASA Ames Research Center Astronautics and Aeronautics, 1986–1990: A Chronology.* (NASA SP-2000-4314, 2000).

GENERAL HISTORIES, NASA SP-4400

Corliss, William R. *NASA Sounding Rockets, 1958–1968: A Historical Summary.* (NASA SP-4401, 1971).

Well, Helen T., Susan H. Whiteley, and Carrie Karegeannes. *Origins of NASA Names.* (NASA SP-4402, 1976).

Anderson, Frank W., Jr. *Orders of Magnitude: A History of NACA and NASA, 1915–1980.* (NASA SP-4403, 1981).

Sloop, John L. *Liquid Hydrogen as a Propulsion Fuel, 1945–1959.* (NASA SP-4404, 1978).

Roland, Alex A. *Spacefaring People: Perspectives on Early Spaceflight.* (NASA SP-4405, 1985).

Bilstein, Roger E. *Orders of Magnitude: A History of the NACA and NASA, 1915–1990.* (NASA SP-4406, 1989).

Logsdon, John M. Editor, with Linda J. Lear, Jannelle Warren-Findley, Ray A. Williamson, and Dwayne A. Day. *Exploring the Unknown: Selected Documents in the History of the U.S. Civil Space Program, Volume I, Organizing for Exploration.* (NASA SP-4407, 1995).

Logsdon, John M. Editor, with Dwayne A. Day and Roger D. Launius. *Exploring the Unknown: Selected Documents in the History of the U.S. Civil Space program, Volume II, Relations with Other Organizations.* (NASA SP-4407, 1996).

Logsdon, John M. Editor, with Roger D. Launius, David H. Onkst, and Stephen E. Garber. *Exploring the Unknown: Selected Documents in the History of the U.S Civil Space Program, Volume III, Using Space.* (NASA SP-4407, 1998).

Logsdon, John M. General Editor, with Ray A. Williamson, Roger D. Launius, Russell J. Acker, Stephen J. Garber, and Jonathan L. Friedman. *Exploring the Unknown: Selected Documents in the History of the U.S. Civil Space Program, Volume IV, Accessing Space.* (NASA SP-4407, 1999).

Logsdon, John M. General Editor, with Amy Paige Snyder, Roger D. Launius, Stephen J. Garber, and Regan Anne Newport. *Exploring the Unknown: Selected Documents in the History of the U.S. Civil Space Program, Volume V, Exploring the Cosmos.* (NASA SP-2001-4407, 2001).

Siddiqi, Asif A. *Challenge to Apollo: The Soviet Union and the Space Race, 1945–1974.* (NASA SP-2000-4408, 2000).

MONOGRAPHS IN AEROSPACE HISTORY, NASA SP-4500

Maisel, Martin D., Demo J. Giulianetti, and Daniel C. Dugan. *The History of the XV-15 Tilt Rotor Research Aircraft: From Concept to Flight.* (NASA SP-2000-4517, 2000).

Jenkins, Dennis R. *Hypersonics Before the Shuttle: A Concise History of the X-15 Research Airplane.* (NASA SP-2000-4518, 2000).

Chambers, Joseph R. *Partners in Freedom: Contributions of the Langley Research Center to U.S. Military Aircraft in the 1990s.* (NASA SP-2000-4519, 2000).

Waltman, Gene L. *Black Magic and Gremlins: Analog Flight Simulations at NASA's Flight Research Center.* (NASA SP-2000-4520, 2000).

Portree, David S. G. *Humans to Mars: Fifty Years of Mission Planning, 1950–2000.* (NASA SP-2001-4521, 2001).

Thompson, Milton O. with J. D. Hunley. *Flight Research: Problems Encountered and What They Should Teach Us.* (NASA SP-2000-4522, 2000).

Tucker, Tom. *The Eclipse Project.* (NASA SP-2000-4523, 2000).

Merlin, Peter W. *Mach 3+: NASA/USAF YF-12 Flight Research, 1969–1979.* (NASA SP-2002-4525, 2002).

Astronaut Garrett Reisman
with Langley Open House
visitors.

NASA Langley photo no. EL-2001-00260.

INDEX

A

B

C

D

E

F

G

H

I

J

K

L

M

N

O

P

R

S

Crafting Flight

W

X

Y

Z

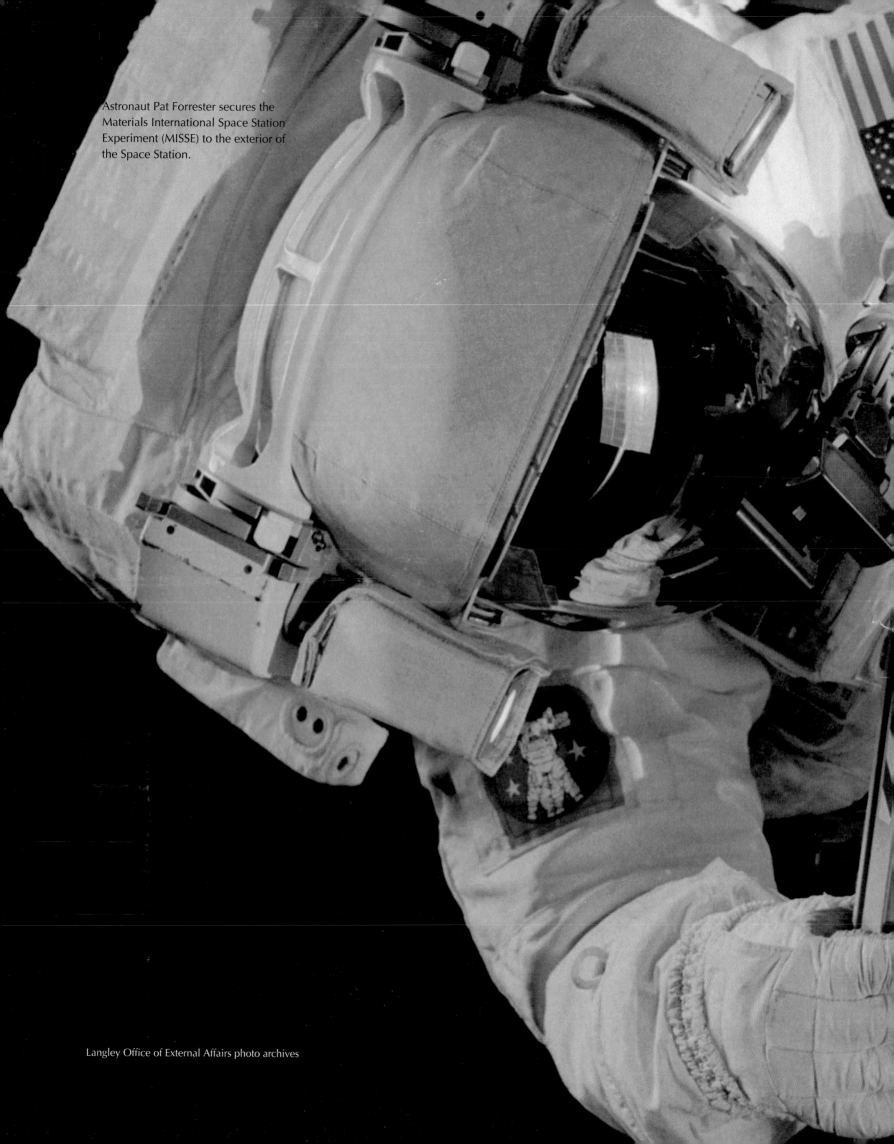

Astronaut Pat Forrester secures the Materials International Space Station Experiment (MISSE) to the exterior of the Space Station.